ROGER'S DODGED OFF ALREADY!
DODGES
WHIZZ!

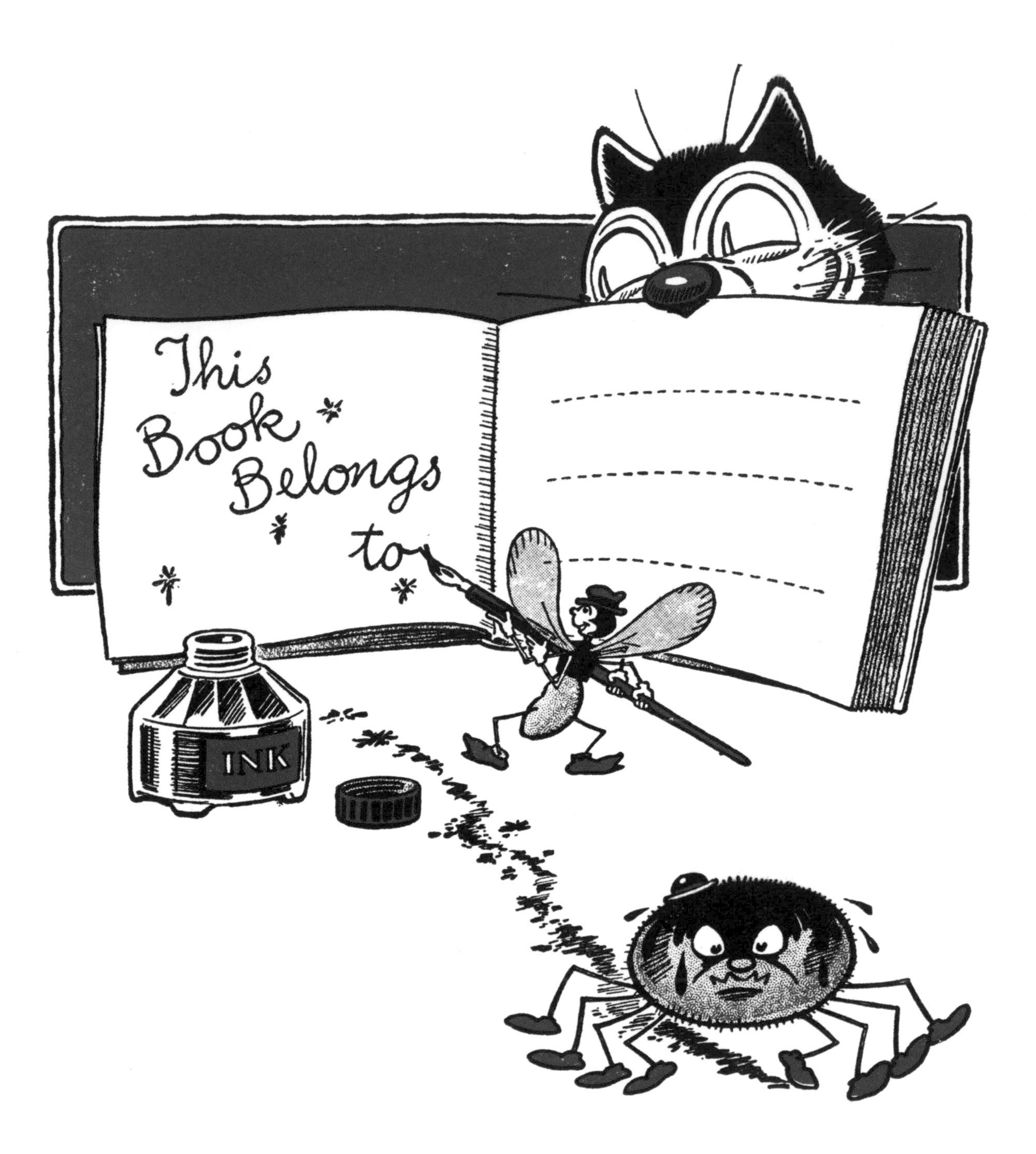

The Classic Beano & Dandy Silly Sing-Along

First published 2013 by DC Thomson Annuals Ltd.
Courier Buildings, 2 Albert Square, Dundee DD1 9QJ
Scotland, UK

www.dcthomson.co.uk
Design and layout by Hugo Breingan
Cover Artwork: Ken Harrison

ISBN: 978-1-84535-510-4
Printed and bound in China

Classic
THE BEANO & THE Dandy
Silly Sing-Along

From the earliest days of The Beano and The Dandy it was clear that many of the characters were musically talented. Some more than others of course and several musically oblivious and tone deaf, but they joined in the fun anyway. This collection of treasures has been lovingly gathered from the musical archives and finely tuned in a new arrangement.

Desperate Dan was one of the most enthusiastic early players showing his passion in unusual ways. For The Bash Street Kids and Dennis The Menace, music is on a scale difficult to beat. Melodic, harmonious and rhythmical it may not always be, but there is always a memorable performance, bearing in mind that the border between music and noise is culturally fine.

There is something for everyone to sing-along to, but you might have to learn some new words to familiar tunes.

THE DANDY MONSTER COMIC
THE MAGIC-BEANO BOOK
DENNIS The Menace 1966
FROM "The BEANO" DENNIS the Menace 1983
THE Dandy BOOK 1974
Rumpity-tumpity-tum! What's that yum-yummy smell from the drum?
THE Beano BOOK 1966
THE DANDY ANNUAL 2008
THE DANDY BOOK 1986
CLASH
OOMPAH
BOOM
CRASH
CLANG
CLAP
CLAP
CLAP
The FROM THE "BEANO" DENNIS the MENACE BOOK 1996
TWANG!
PLONK!
BEANO TOWN TALENT CONTEST
THE DANDY BOOK 1999

MUSIC SHOP
GRAND MUSICAL ~CONTEST.~ BUY A MUSICAL INSTRUMENT AND ENTER.
GEE, I SHOULD CHOOSE SOMETHING TO PLAY AND GO IN FOR THIS.
TRUMPETS • DRUMS • FIDD
HORNS

IN THE SHOP
TRY THIS TRUMPET, SIR, BUT YOU'LL HAVE TO TAKE THE BOWLER HAT OFF THE MOUTH OF IT FIRST.
UNFORTUNATELY, DAN DOESN'T HEAR.
TRUMPET

THERE'S SOMETHING WRONG WITH THIS PESKY TRUMPET!
STOP BLOWING, SIR, IT'S THE BOWLER HAT THAT'S KEEPING THE AIR IN.
TRUMPET

HUH! THAT'S A FUNNY KIND OF TRUMPET. I JUST GAVE IT A BIT OF A PUFF~ AND IT'S BUST LIKE A BALLOON!
BANG
BUMP

THIS IS BETTER~A NICE BIG MAN-SIZED FIDDLE. BUT THE SPIKE STICKING IN MY CHIN IS A BIT OF A NUISANCE.
SCRAPE

AW, SHUCKS! I'VE SAWN THE PESKY FIDDLE IN HALF!
SAW

NOW THAT'S A VERY EXPENSIVE INSTRUMENT, DAN. PLEASE BE CAREFUL WITH IT!

DRAT IT! I'VE BLOWN SO HARD THAT THE HORN HAS STARTED TO UNWIND NOW, AND IT'S SPINNING ME ROUND WITH IT!
BLAST
PUSH

MY-MY! EVERYTHING IS SURE SPINNING FAST. I FEEL DIZZY.
TO PIANOS
DRUMS

I CAN'T STAND STRAIGHT. OOPS! NOW WHAT'S THIS I'M FALLING ON?~IT'S THE BIG DRUM! I HOPE THE SKIN IS TOUGH!
TO PIANO
DONG

WAY OUT
PONG
PLANG
BOUNCE
GRAND PIANO
IT'S TOUGH ALL RIGHT! IT'S BOUNCED ME UP INTO THE AIR AGAIN.

MUSIC SHOP
WHEN WILL THIS STOP? NOW THE PIANO IS RUNNING AWAY ON TO THE STREET WITH ME.

PAWNB
HUH! I'M JAMMED IN THE TRAM-LINES AND HERE'S A PESKY TRAM-CAR COMING.

HEY, YOU! GET OFF THAT PIANO. GOSH! WHERE'S THE GUY I SAW SITTING THERE?
WHIZZ
PAWNBROKER
SNAP
PING
CRASH

THAT BRASS BALL MADE A NICE MUSICAL NOISE WHEN IT DROPPED ON TO THE LETTER-BOX. THAT GIVES ME AN IDEA.
TING-TING

JUNK YARD
OLD IRON SOLD HERE
NOW I'VE GOT ALL I NEED FOR A REAL HE-MAN MUSICAL INSTRUMENT.

THE MUSICAL CONTEST
THE NEXT COMPETITOR IS DESPERATE DAN. HE WILL PLAY "THE BELLS OF ST. CLEMENTS"~ OOH! WHAT A DIN!
TING
DONG
CLANG
MANHOLE LID
WHAT A ROW
SOME MUSIC THIS.
FAINTED
IT'S BUSTING MY EAR DRUMS.

THIS WAY, FIREMEN! AIM YOUR HOSES THROUGH THE WINDOW!
HUH! WE THOUGHT ALL THE NOISE COMING FROM HERE WAS A FIRE ALARM ~BUT IT'S ONLY DAN GIVING A CONCERT. STOP THE WATER, BOYS.
D. WATKINS

The Dandy August 26th, 1950.

The Dandy February 16th, 1952.

TAP! TAP!
TINKLE!
PLONK!
TWANG!
BOOM!
BANGA!
BOOM!
SQUEAK!
TOOT!
BANG!
DOINK!
POUND!
DINK!
BLART!
BOING!
BOOMEDY!
PEEP!
BOOM!
DING!
BONG!
CLAP!
SCREECH!
BOOM!
BOOMEDY!
BOOM!
The Bash Street Kids
THE HEAD ORDERED ME TO BRING THIS LOT TO THE SYMPHONY CONCERT TO MAKE THEM APPRECIATE MUSIC, BUT I THINK IT'S A RISK!
BEETHOVEN
FOR OUR FIRST ITEM, WE WILL PLAY "BRAHMS' LULLABY"
SNIP
SWEET MUSIC
CRUMP!
SNORES
SNORES
SHAME
SWEET DREAMS
SNORE
THEN—
GOODY! — THE KIDS SHOULD ENJOY THIS.
PROGRAMME ITEM 2— "THE DANCE of the SUGAR PLUM FAIRY"
SO SHE'S A SUGAR PLUM FAIRY, EH? LET'S GIVE HER SOME SUGAR ~
~AN' SOME NICE ROTTEN PLUMS!
SQUELCH!
SPLUDGE
SPLODGE
SUGAR LUMPS
ROTTEN PLUMS
ROTTEN PLUMS
PING
PING
PING
NEXT, WE ARE GOING TO HAVE "HANDEL'S WATER MUSIC."
OOH! I AM GETTING MAD!
SNIGGER
YOU SUPPLY THE MUSIC, WE'LL SUPPLY THE WATER! HEH! HEH! HEH!
I NEW THIS WOULD HAPPEN!
OOMPAH MUSIC OOMP OOMP OOMP
GRRR! WE WILL NOW PLAY "THE CHARGE OF THE LIGHT CAVALRY"
YOU HEARD WHAT HE SAID ~ PREPARE TO CHARGE, BASH ST. LIGHT CAVALRY.
HYSTERICAL GIGGLES
LIGHT CAVALRY
EMERGENCY! LOWER THE ASBESTOS FIRE-CURTAIN! QUICKLY!
EMERGENCY ASBESTOS FIRE CURTAIN
BAM!
CRUMP!
CRUMP!
THUD!
QUICK, GRAB THEM WHILE THEY ARE STILL DAZED - HEH, HEH!
GROAN!
OOOH!
CLASH!
CRUNCH!
NOW WE'LL HAVE A TUNE WITH A LITTLE MORE BEAT IN IT! HEE! HEE!
WHACK!
WHACK!
ENCORE! MORE! MORE!
DRUM MUSIC BOOM BOOM BOOM
TWANG! DOINK! BONG! CLAP! POUND! PEEP! SQUEAK! BOING! BLART!

DINK! PLONK! TOOT! SCREECH! TWANG! DOINK! BONG! CLAP! POUND!

the Bash Street Kids
LOOK! THIS IS A CERTIFICATE MY CLASS WON ON A RADIO QUIZ GAME!
THIS IS A CERTIFICATE MY CLASS WON IN THE INTER-SCHOOLS SWIMMING RELAY!
JEALOUSY
CERTIFICATE
THE BASH ST. KIDS' TEACHER
IT'S THE INTER-SCHOOLS MUSIC FESTIVAL TOMORROW AND I'VE ENTERED YOU LOT IN THE CHOIR SECTION. IF YOU PRACTISE HARD YOU'LL WIN A CERTIFICATE AND KEEP UP WITH THE OTHER CLASSES!
SUCK
SUCK
SUCK
HOW PRETTY!
NYMPHS AND SHEPHERDS COME AWAY.
STILL SUCKING IN BREATH
COME AWAY
A WORD IN THOSE DUSTBIN-LIDS YOU CALL EARS — WE'LL NEVER WIN A CERTIFICATE WITH YOU IN THE CHOIR SO YOU SIT DOWN AND SHUSH!
BAW! WAH! I WANNA BE IN THE CHOIR
BOO HOO!
BAW!
THE GOVERNORS ARE MAKING A SURPRISE VISIT TO THE SCHOOL. FOR GOODNESS SAKE STOP PLUG MAKING THAT ROW OR THE GOVERNORS WILL THINK WE'RE ILL-TREATING THE KIDS!
BOO HOO BAW!
ALL RIGHT, ALL RIGHT, IF YOU'LL STOP BAWLING YOU CAN BE IN THE CHOIR!
OOH TA!
AND AT THE FESTIVAL
NYMPHS AND SHEPHERDS COME AWAY
COME AWAY!
AND THAT'S JUST WHAT THE AUDIENCE DO!
COME AWAY!
STAMPEDE
BUT ONE MAN REMAINS! GOSH, IS HE CRACKERS?
WHAT A SMASHING VOICE!
SLAM
I LIKE YOUR VOICE — IF YOU'LL COME AND SING FOR ME, I'LL BUY YOU ICE-CREAM AND SWEETS FOR A WEEK!
!
WE'RE NEARLY THERE, YOUNG FELLER-ME-LAD!
COO, IT'S AWFUL FOGGY!
DAISY, DAISY, GIVE ME YOUR ANSWER DO-OOO-OOOO!!
THE FOGHORN HAS BROKEN DOWN — BUT THAT LAD'S VOICE IS BETTER THAN ANY FOGHORN!
NOW I'VE GOT A CERTIFICATE FOR ONE OF MY PUPILS!
?
PRIDE
THIS IS TO CERTIFY THAT PLUG IS THE BEST FOGHORN I'VE EVER HEARD.
Signed

WHEN THE BELL RINGS
WILFRID
HERBERT
SMIFFY
DANNY
PLUG
FATTY
JIMMY
BIG FELLA
ALL IS PEACEFUL IN BASH ST. SCHOOL UNTIL-
YEOWL
SCREECH
SQUEAK
TWO NEW BOYS HAVE ARRIVED ALL THE WAY FROM BONNIE SCOTLAND
I'LL JUST TAKE A NOTE OF YOUR NAMES!
WILLIE MACKINTOSH AND SANDY MACKINTOSH. YOU'RE TWINS, I SEE!
WHILE TEACHER'S BUSY WE'LL DODGE OUT FOR A GAME OF FOOTBALL!
SUFFERING CATS! THESE BAGPIPES HAVE GIVEN THE GAME AWAY!
YEOWL
4 O'CLOCK AND THE BASH ST. KIDS HAVE BEEN KEPT IN AS PUNISHMENT.
CHEERIO, CHAPS!
BE GOOD!
BONK!
NEXT DAY. WHAT'S GONE WRONG WITH THE KIDS? THE SUN'S SHINING AND THEY'RE ALL WEARING WATERPROOFS!
FINE WEATHER WE'RE HAVING!
SLURP
PLEASE, TEACHER, WHAT WILL WE DO WITH THE MACKINTOSHES?
HANG THEM UP IN THE CLOAKROOM, OF COURSE, YOU DIM LOT!
GOOD!
WE ALWAYS DO AS TEACHER TELLS US!
'S NICE AND PEACEFUL IN CLASS AGAIN. CARRY ON SLEEPING, CHAPS!
ZZZZ

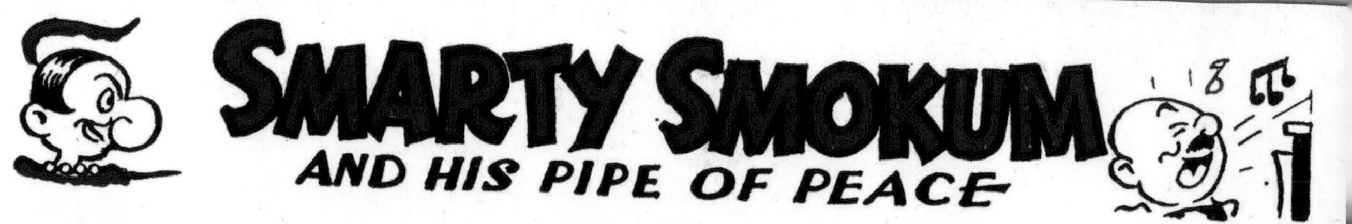

"For goodness sake, be quiet there,"
Old Smarty hears a Pa declare.
"Your crying drives me to despair."

Cries Smarty Smokum, "Cheer up, Dad,
"I'll soon stop Baby being bad."
He blows some smoke upon the lad.

Now Baby's good as good can be.
Pa says, "You really must join me.
We'll sing a little song, you see."

A song is what Pa most enjoys.
The two sing like a pair of boys.
But Baby says, "Coo, what a noise!"

The pipe of peace then Baby spies.
He blows some smoke in Smokum's eyes.
The two men then heave weary sighs.

Then Pa and Smarty Smokum fall
Into a sleep against the wall,
While Baby just laughs at it all.

TWANG! DOINK! BONG! CLAP! POUND! PEEP! SQUEAK! BOING! BLART!

Poor Smarty wears a frown,
For he can't calm things down.

And he wants peace—but wait!
Just see what's on that plate!

SMARTY SMOKUM AND HIS PIPE OF PEACE

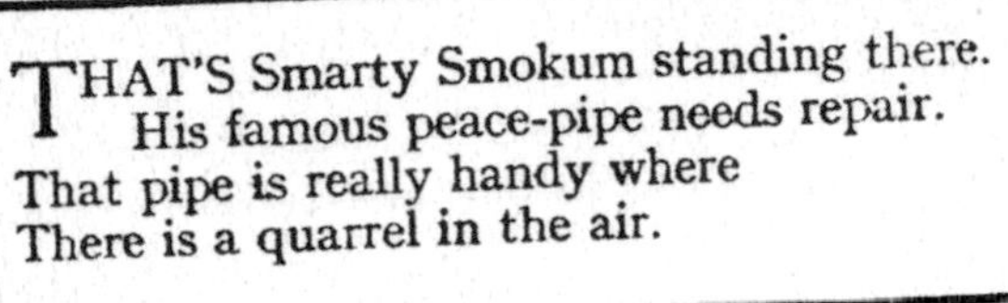

THAT'S Smarty Smokum standing there.
His famous peace-pipe needs repair.
That pipe is really handy where
There is a quarrel in the air.

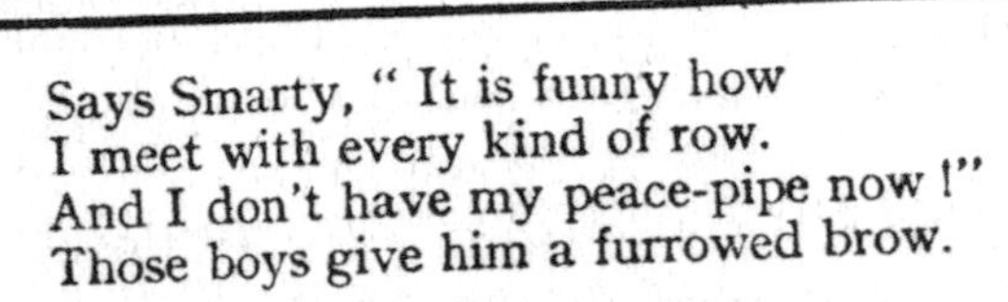

Says Smarty, " It is funny how
I meet with every kind of row.
And I don't have my peace-pipe now !"
Those boys give him a furrowed brow.

That barrel organ is off key,
And Smarty mutters, " Woe is me.
Oh, gosh, if only I could be
Alone—away far out at sea."

At last our chum can stand no more.
" Peace! Give me peace !" hear Smarty roar.
That cafe owner at the door
Says, " You should have come here before."

Now Smarty Smokum's yanked inside.
His gaping mouth is open wide.
He feels that he should run and hide.
" I'll fix you," says the boss with pride.

Just look at Smarty, if you please !
Instead of peace our lad gets peas.
But soon he smiles at what he sees,
And eats them. Then he's more at ease.

Old Winnie Witch says, " Ah, I see
My new house is complete.
I'll fetch my furniture," says she,
" And make the place look neat."

Then home she goes. Cries, " Fiddle-dee !"
For that's her magic word.
" Come, furniture, and walk with me."
It really looks absurd.

Then with her magic trumpet, Win
Walks to her new abode ;
She really makes a frightful din
As she struts down the road.

As Winnie walks and gaily blows,
A circus band goes by.
" That stuff would look good in our shows,"
Just hear the driver cry.

Their big brass band then starts to play
And drowns poor Winnie's tune.
The furniture turns round their way.
It makes the old witch swoon.

" Come back," she cries, and waves her hand.
Her furniture has gone.
For it keeps following the band,
And marches on and on.

TWANG! DOINK! BONG! CLAP! POUND! PEEP! SQUEAK! BOING! BLART!

TAP! TAP!
TINKLE!
PLONK!
TWANG!
BOOM!
BANGA!
BOOM!
SQUEAK!
TOOT!
BANG!
DOINK!
POUND!
DINK!
BLART!
BOING!
BOOMEDY!
PEEP!
BOOM!
DING!
BONG!
CLAP!
SCREECH!
BOOM!
BOOMEDY!
BOOM!

DINK! PLONK! TOOT! SCREECH! TWANG! DOINK! BONG! CLAP! POUND!

VARIETY SHOW
MUM! THE BOSS GAVE ME TICKETS FOR A VARIETY SHOW! TOO BAD HE GAVE ME THREE. WE'LL HAVE TO TAKE DENNIS!
AHA! VARIETY IS THE SPICE!
GOING IN
COME ON, MUGS! GET YOUR GREAT BIG FEET OUTA MY WAY!
YOU'RE ALWAYS DOING THE WRONG THING, DENNIS. YOU'VE MADE EVERYBODY ANGRY WITH YOUR CHEEK!
I'LL LIVEN THIS ACT UP A BIT!
HA-HA-HA!
HO-HO-HO!
ALWAYS DOING THE WRONG THING!
THAT WAS THE RIGHT THING. ALL THE PEOPLE ARE LAUGHING, AREN'T THEY?
NO! YOU'RE NOT THROWING THAT TOMATO!
IF I CAN'T THROW THE TOMATO, I WANT ICE-CREAM!
SH! SH! SH!
I'VE GOT ICE-CREAM BUT I'M NOT EATING IT!
DENNIS! WHAT A THING TO DO!
SEEMS TO BE SOMETHING BLOCKING THIS!
IT WAS THEM! LOOK! THEY'RE EATING ICE-CREAM!
GO! AND NEVER DARKEN OUR SEVEN-AND-SIXPENNY SEATS AGAIN!
DENNIS AGAIN! JUST WAIT!
HO, HO! I ALWAYS ENJOY MYSELF BETTER WITHOUT THEM!
LATER SO YOU'RE BACK, EH? I'M TIRED OF YOU ALWAYS DOING THE WRONG THING!
PUT DENNIS TO BED, AND PUT THE MILK BOTTLES OUT!
RIGHT!
ONE MINUTE WHILE I PUT THE MILK BOTTLES TO BED!
NOW I'LL PUT YOU OUT!
HOW D'YOU LIKE WHEN I DO THE WRONG THING?
IT MUST BE GREAT TO HAVE A ROOF OVER YOUR HEAD!

CAROL CHUCKLES
GRACIOUS!
WHAT'S THAT?
EEE-EEE-OW-EEE-OW
CHRISTMAS EVE
IT'S DENNIS~ PRACTISING CAROLS!
GOOD KING WENCESLAS
EE-OW EE-OW EE-OW OW-OW
HE'S OFF TO SING CAROLS IN THE STREET. THAT TOFFEE SHOULD KEEP HIM QUIET UNTIL HE'S WELL AWAY FROM HERE!
YUM YUM
THIS IS WHERE FATTY DIXON LIVES, I'LL SING HIM A CAROL!
GOOD KING WENCESLAS LOOKED OUT
SPLOSH!
HO-HO! THAT'S FATTY DIXON LOOKING OUT TO SEE WHO'S SINGING -AND I'VE A SNOWBALL READY FOR HIM!
DENNIS TRIES THE SAME DODGE FARTHER DOWN THE STREET.
GOOD KING WENCESLAS LOOKED OUT
AS SOON AS THE WINDOW OPENS~I'LL LET 'EM HAVE IT!
YOU'RE SHAKIN' THE PLASTER OFF MY CEILING! SCRAM!
BAH! HE DIDN'T USE THE WINDOW!
SLAM
HELP! THE SNOW'S BEEN SHAKEN OFF THE ROOF!
A LITTLE LATER
I'VE GOT ANOTHER IDEA! I'LL PUT ON MY FANCY MASK!
GOOD KING WENCESLAS LOOKED OUT
HO-HO-HO! AM I HAVIN' A GOOD TIME!
LATER
HI, DENNIS! WE'RE HAVING A PARTY FOR PEOPLE IN THE STREET. COME AND SING FOR US!
YOU'LL FIND A MOST APPRECIATIVE AUDIENCE HERE. WE'VE ALL HEARD YOU SINGING TONIGHT!
GLARE
HATE
REVENGE
HERE'S THE LAD WHO WAS SINGING IN OUR STREET!
GOOD KING-OUCH!-ESLAS LOOKED OUCH!
ATTA-BOY, DENNIS. SING UP, LAD!
REVENGE!
YOU'RE DOING FINE, DENNIS!
I'VE BEEN SINGING CAROLS, DAD!
CHRISTMAS MORNING
SANTA CLAUS MUST THINK YOU LIKE CAROLS, DENNIS!
WE'RE KIDDING HIM. WE'LL LET HIM HAVE HIS REAL TOYS IN A MINUTE!
XMAS CAROLS

BILLY WHIZZ
STOP, BILLY! STOP! YOU'RE PLAYING TOO FAST!
SCHOOL ORCHESTRA
IT SHOULD TAKE AN HOUR TO PLAY THIS PIECE—YOU FINISHED IT IN THREE MINUTES!
COO! IS THAT A WORLD RECORD, SIR?
SOKSOFFSKI'S 12th SYMPHONY
TRY PLAYING THE VIOLIN.
WHIZZ!
ZZZZ!
OH, NO! YOU'VE SAWN IT IN HALF WITH YOUR HIGH-SPEED PLAYING! HERE, TAKE THIS TROMBONE AND SLOW DOWN!
BUT—
CRUMBS! HE'S PLAYING SO FAST THE TROMBONE'S BEGINNING TO GLOW RED HOT!
TA-RAH-TA-RAH!
STOP! STOP!
AAAH!
SIZZLE!

CLANG! CLANG! CLANG! CLANG! CLANG!
PERHAPS BILLY COULD PLAY THE TRIANGLE — NO! THE PUPILS MIGHT THINK IT WAS THE SCHOOL BELL, AND RUN FOR THE GATE!
JUST YOU GO HOME, BILLY—THERE'S A GOOD BOY!
BUT, SIR—
LOOK, READERS! BILLY'S ACTUALLY WALKING! WHY NOT KEEP THIS VERY UNUSUAL PICTURE?
THERE MUST BE SOME INSTRUMENT I CAN PLAY.
CUT ROUND DOTTED LINE
HELLO, TONI! WHAT'S THE MATTER?
I'M ALL PUFFED OUT TURNING THE HANDLE OF MY BARREL-ORGAN!
HA! HA! AT LAST I'VE FOUND AN INSTRUMENT I CAN PLAY AS FAST AS I LIKE!
ZOOM!
LITTLE LION

THE DITTY OF
DENNIS THE MENACE
TO THE TUNE OF "JOHN PEEL"
Yes, you all know me, dressed in black and red—
Dad would rather have a tiger instead.
Folks sigh with relief when I'm off to bed—
But I'll be up an' doin' in the morning.
Then the sound of the whacks will ring through the town
As Dad's slipper blows come a-raining down.
You can hear this each day, even far far away
Like a carpet-beating works in the morning.
I was five years old when I went to school—
It took me an hour to break every rule,
Teacher was boiling, but I kept him cool
With a shower-bath of ink in the morning!
Then the sound of the whacks . . . . . .
What? Keep tadpole pets? Huh! Pardon my smile!
The truth is that tadpoles are not my style.
I remember when Dad found my crocodile
A-swimming in his bath in the morning.
Then the sound of the whacks . . . .
That old chap John Peel used to hunt the fox.
But it's not much fun givin' Reynard socks.
Me, I fix a snare to the letter-box
Just to catch a postman in the morning!
Then the sound of the whacks . . . . . .

The
BASH
STREET
KIDS

Bad news does not amuse!
T-TEACHER, IT'S TERRIBLE...READ THIS!
THERE, THERE, HEAD! CALM YOURSELF! IT CAN'T BE THAT BAD!
BUT—
AGH! THEY CAN'T DO THIS TO ME!
EDUCATION COMMITTEE NOTICE
ALL SCHOOLS WILL ENTER THEIR IIB CLASSES FOR A MUSICAL COMPETITION IN THE TOWN HALL NEXT WEEK
WHAT CAN YOUR PUPILS PLAY, TEACHER?
THEY CAN ONLY PLAY TRUANT!

Learning to play Teacher's way!
BUT I AM A TEACHER... SO I'LL TEACH THEM MUSIC...IF ONLY THEY HAD BRAINS!
LATER—
BLAB!BLAB! THAT IS THE TASK. NOW CAN ANYONE PLAY A MUSICAL INSTRUMENT?
NOT ME, TEACHER!
NO, SIR!
NOR ME!
LATER—
NOW YOU MUST LEARN TO PLAY THESE INSTRUMENTS I'VE BORROWED FROM THE SCHOOL ORCHESTRA!

BUT—
PLONK!
PARP!
PING!
OOMPAH!
SEVERAL REHEARSALS LATER—
GROAN! THEY'RE AS BAD AS EVER! I'LL HAVE TO ASK PROFESSOR PLUNKETT, THE FAMOUS MUSICIAN, TO LEND A HAND!
TERRIBLE DIN
GHASTLY NOISE
SOON—
I'M PROFESSOR PLUNKETT. I CAN SEE YOU NEED HELP!
GASP! WE'RE TIRED OUT—AND SO ARE OUR INSTRUMENTS!

Grand band!

THE KIDS MUST ONLY PLAY INSTRUMENTS THEY LIKE,OR THEY WILL NEVER LEARN!
INDEED?
NOW, KIDS, WHAT WOULD YOU LIKE TO PLAY?
WE KNOW WHAT WE'D LIKE TO PLAY!
CONTEST DAY—
THEY WON THE CONTEST! WHAT DID THEY PLAY? WELL, LISTEN TO THE ENCORE!
SCHOOLS' MUSIC COMPETITION
"BEANO" IS BEST! YEAH! YEAH!
The BEANO BEATERS

108
THE BASH STREET KIDS
THINK WE'LL ORGANISE AN OLD-TIME SONG-WRITING CONTEST TO PROVE THAT THE OLD STUFF IS BETTER THAN MODERN POP RUBBISH!
GOOD IDEA, HEAD!
TUNING FORK
DOH-H-H!
SO—
START COMPOSING BEAUTIFUL SONGS LIKE WE ENJOYED IN THE GOOD OLD DAYS!
HNF!
I'LL HAVE A GO AT SONG-WRITING MYSELF!
TINKLE! TINKLE!
TUM-TEE-TUM-TIDDLETY-TOODLE-
I'LL GET YOU YET!

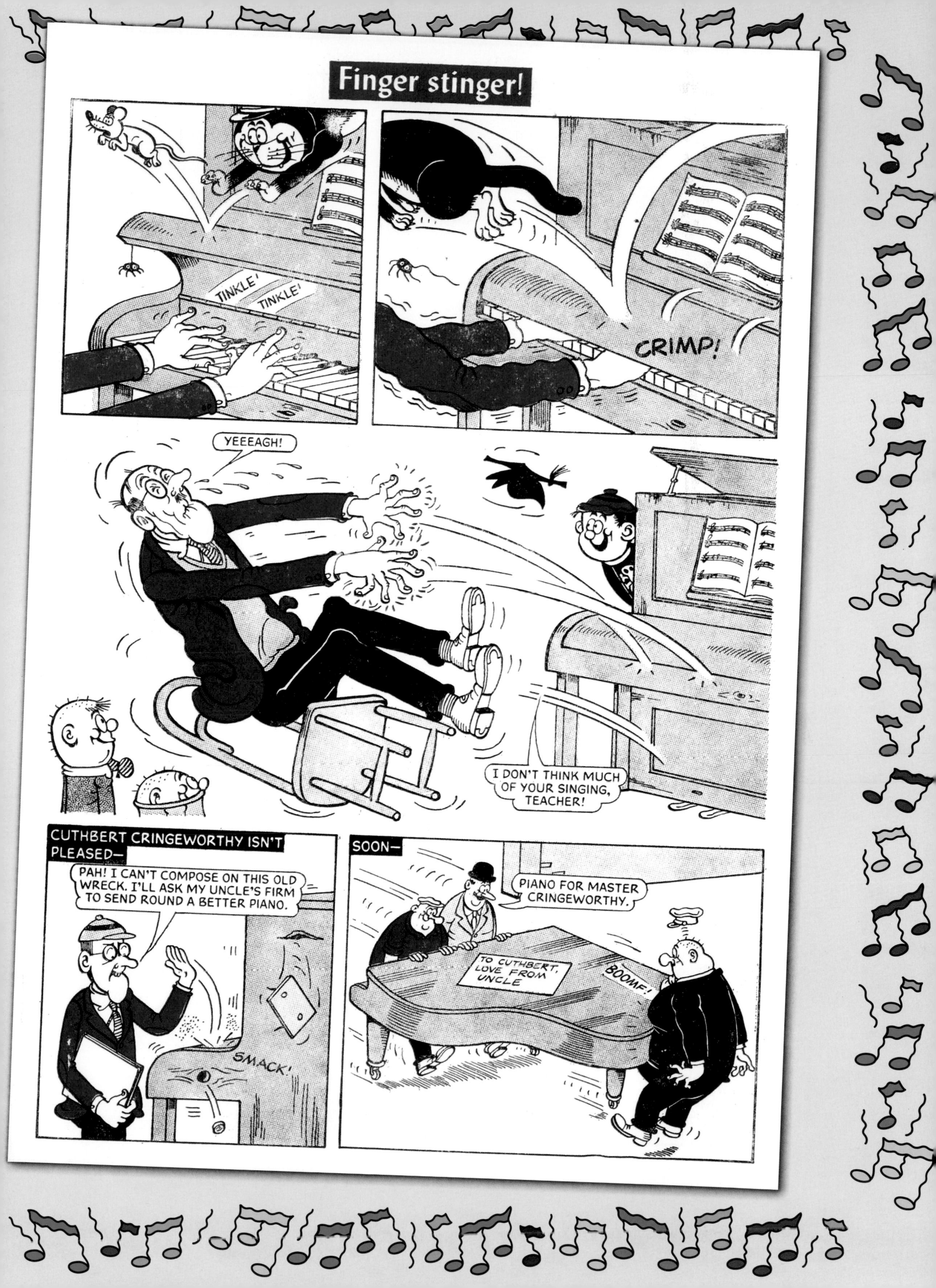
Finger stinger!
TINKLE!
TINKLE!
CRIMP!
YEEEAGH!
I DON'T THINK MUCH OF YOUR SINGING, TEACHER!
CUTHBERT CRINGEWORTHY ISN'T PLEASED—
PAH! I CAN'T COMPOSE ON THIS OLD WRECK. I'LL ASK MY UNCLE'S FIRM TO SEND ROUND A BETTER PIANO.
SMACK!
SOON—
PIANO FOR MASTER CRINGEWORTHY.
TO CUTHBERT, LOVE FROM UNCLE
BOOMF!

Tight fit—smash hit!
I'LL SOON GET IT INTO CLASS II B.
TO CUTHBERT! LOVE FROM UNCLE
BUT—
SMASH!
GULP! THE DOOR'S TOO NARROW!
THEN—
WHAT'S THAT?
IT'S SUPPOSED TO BE A GRAND PIANO.
HUMPH! IT DOESN'T LOOK VERY GRAND TO ME!
FATTY'S MEANT TO BE COMPOSING A TUNE ON THE OOMPAH, BUT HE'S NOT MAKING MUCH NOISE!
PARP!
IT MAKES A LOVELY FOOD-SAFE!

Fancy that—a musical cat!
THE CRUNCH OF A PIE CRUST IS MUSIC TO MY EARS!
THAT'S VERY GOOD! WONDER WHO'S PLAYING IT?
I CAN'T THINK OF ANYTHING.
CLASS AQUARIUM
SPLASH!

112
A song by Smiffy in a jiffy!
COO! THAT LOOKS GOOD! I'LL MAKE A COPY OF IT!
ONE COPY LATER—
THANKS, PALS! BACK YOU GO INTO THE JAR!
LATER—
WELL DONE, SMIFFY, MY BOY! YOUR BEAUTIFUL "TADPOLE CONCERTO" WINS THE CONTEST EASILY!
TADPOLE CONCERTO BY SMIFFY
THANK YOU, HEAD!
YAHOO!

THE BEANO
IT'S CHRISTMAS!
No 2684 DECEMBER 25th 1993
EVERY THURSDAY 35p
DENNIS the MENACE and GNASHER
THROW
THROW
WELL I'M HANGIN' UP A SOFTY ON THE WALL — IT'S THE TIME WHEN EVERY MENACE HAS A BALL.
CLIP ON
SING TO SLADE'S "MERRY CHRISTMAS EVERYBODY"
IF YOU HAVEN'T ANY REINDEER, USE A PIG TO PULL YOUR SLEIGH. BETTER WATCH OUT, DAD - YOU'VE GOT RIGHT IN THE WAY!
TOPPLE
SPLAT
OINKEE!

WELL HERE IT IS, MERRY CHRISTMAS, GOOD OLD GNASHER'S HAVING FUN. SITS BY THE FIRESIDE AND BITES SANTA UP THE BUM.
BITE
THROW
YIKES!
SUM BOOK
FOR DENNIS
THROB
HAR! HAR!
ARE YOU WAITING FOR THE SOFTIES TO ARRIVE?
POLISH
RUB
POLISH
HAVE YOU POLISHED UP THE ICE THAT'S IN YOUR DRIVE?
SKID
SLIP
THUMP
SLIP

DOES YOUR GRANNY ALWAYS TELL YOU, PUT SOME FLEAS DOWN WALTER'S VEST?
SHAKE
FLEAS
TUG
HE'LL BE UP SOON ROCK AN' ROLLIN' WITH THE BEST.
SCRATCH
SCRATCH
WELL HERE IT IS, MERRY CHRISTMAS. HOPE YOU ALL HAVE LOTS OF FUN. EAT LOTS OF TURKEY AND SCOFF PLUM PUD BY THE TON.
TUG
GNASHER
ADVANCED MATHS
HISTORY
ART
SCIENCE
MUM AND DAD'S WISH
PULL
WISH BONE
ICE CREAM
JOKE
MERRY XMAS DAD

THE STORY FROM THE COVER

Pup Group

YOWL! ***No, readers, it's not the cry of an ape-man—it's only little me, your favourite menace, practising for our singing lesson at school today.***

I set off for school at my usual brisk crawl about ten past nine and managed to arrive in time to miss the first maths period.

Then we all trooped into the music room where Teacher was going to select a choir to sing for the school in the Musical Festival. YUGH! Musical Festivals are soppy. Why can't we have a Pea-shooting Festival or a Mud-throwing Festival or something worthwhile like that?

All the boys in our class had to sing "Oh, for the wings of a dove!"

Yeeouch! Now if it had been "Oh, for the wings of a turkey!" I might have been interested.

My favourite enemy, Walter, was selected to sing the solo.

He was solo, all right! So low, I couldn't hear him but Teacher seemed to be pleased!

Then my turn came, so I gave my tough tonsils a twitch and warbled, "OH FOR THE WINGS OF A VULTURE!"

"Enough!" bellowed Teacher, with his fingers in his ears. "Fly from this room and never return!"

Later on, in the playground I bumped into Walter.

"You nasty rotter," he lisped, picking himself off the ground. "You're just jealous because you've been put out of the choir and we're going to win and get a super feed!"

"Huh!" I scoffed, a bit more interested now that a super feed had been mentioned.

"Bet I could get a choir together that would knock spots off you lot!"

However, it wasn't so easy getting a choir together as I thought! All my pals were in the school choir—or were they?

My best pal wasn't in any choir. You see my best pal is Gnasher, my trusty dog.

"That's it!" The idea suddenly hit me like a rotten tomato splattering on Walter's nose!

"I'll get a dog choir started and enter it for the festival!"

"Get all your pals together, Gnasher!" I ordered. "And meet for rehearsal in Gasworks Lane!"

Soon Gnasher had gathered a goodly collection of pals to join the choir—Jasper the Bulldog, Abdul the Afghan Hound, Al the St. Bernard and several other four-footed friends.

"Pay attention, songsters," I said, tapping with my conductor's baton. "We're going to call the choir "THE HAPPY HOWLERS" and we'll start off by singing "GRANNY WOULDN'T BUY ME A BOW-WOW!"

There's mischief afoot—When Korky goes toot-er-oot!
Korky THE CAT
GOSH! THIS BOOK HAS GIVEN ME A WIZARD IDEA!
THE PIED PIPER of HAMELIN
MUSIC SHOP
I'VE BOUGHT A TOOTLER! IF THE PIED PIPER USED ONE TO LURE RATS ALONG, I COULD USE ONE ON MICE.
ALL KINDS of MUSICAL INSTRUMENTS
I'LL DO SOME PRACTISING!
TOOTLE-TOOT
MUSIC for BEGINNERS
But the mice have found Korky's book—
TOOTLE-OOO TOOT
SO THAT'S HIS GAME!
THE PIED PIPER of HAMELIN
I KNOW! LET'S MAKE HIM THINK HIS PLAN IS WORKING.
And so—
TOOTLE
DRIED PEAS
HERE HE COMES, LADS— LET HIM HAVE IT!
OUCH! WOW! A BOMBARDMENT OF ROTTEN FRUIT!
WHIZZ
WHIZZZ
WHOOSH
DRIED PEAS
HEE-HEE! WE FOOLED YOU GOOD AND PROPER!
HAW-HAW! EVER BEEN HAD, KORKY?
SLAM
THAT'S WHAT YOU THINK! BUT I'VE FOOLED YOU. I'VE GOT THE LOT OF YOU OUT IN THE OPEN— WHERE I WANT YOU!
DRIED PEAS

TAKE THAT!
DRIED PEAS
SPRAY
OUCH!
PING
PING
EEK!
OOYAH!
AARGH!
PING
PING
PING
PING
PING
PING
PING
YIKE!
HA-HA! I DIDN'T ONLY LEAD THEM OUT, I LAID THEM OUT AS WELL!
OW!
OOOH!
GROAN!
OUCH!
ZZZ

THE BASH STREET KIDS
HERE ARE YOUR TICKETS FOR THE CLASS DANCE, IN THE SCHOOL HALL, AT SEVEN O'CLOCK TONIGHT!
CLASS IIB
FLIP
DANCE
GRAB
DANCE
So—
YEH, LET'S DANCE!
SNAP
SNAP
SCHOOL DANCE Tonight
BASH ST. SCHOOL

WHERE DO YOU UNRULY MOB THINK YOU'RE GOING?
SCHOOL HALL
SHOW TICKETS AT DOOR
IT'S ME, TEACHER!
AARGH! SO IT IS! KEEP THOSE DARK GLASSES ON!
PUSH
I THOUGHT THIS MIGHT HAPPEN! CHANGE INTO THESE EXTRA SCHOOL UNIFORMS!
KIDS' SCHOOL UNIFORMS

HUH! SOME DANCE THIS IS GOING TO BE.
VERY LOUD POP MUSIC
EEAGH!
YOU CAN'T DANCE TO THAT MUSIC . . .
TWOINNG!
SNIP
TWOING
SNIP
YE GRAMOPHONE
WIND

COME ON — TAKE YOUR PARTNERS, ALL JOIN IN!
TWIRL
SPIN
COME HERE OFTEN?
BOOMFF!
TWIST
SPIN
GROAN! THIS IS THE WORST DANCE EVER!
WHAT DID YOU THINK OF THAT, KIDS?
BOW

–
100
PATHETIC
TERRY
BULL
AWFUL
-10
–O
+O
TIME FOR A GAME!
HMMM . . .
CLICK!
WE'LL PLAY AT THE GHOSTS OF BASH STREET . . .
CLICK!
THAT'S NOT A PARTY GAME . . .

RING-A-RING A ROSES . . .
WHIRL!
AW, NO!
SPIN
TEACHER, TEACHER! THIS ISN'T THE KIND OF DANCE ANYBODY LIKES NOWADAYS!
OH, ISN'T IT, HEAD?
CLASS IIB
BLAST OF POP MUSIC
DONK
SPIN
HOOCH KOOCH
DOO-A-DEE DEE!
THROW
GOOD RHYTHM, SMIFFY!
WELL, IF YOU CAN'T BEAT THEM!

HOW TO PLAY INSTRUMENTS
SOAPY LIQUID
Coronet—
ER — THAT'S NOT THE RIGHT KIND OF CORNET, DENNIS.
SPLAT
ICE-CREAM CORNET
Mouth organ—
CAN'T GET A SOUND OUT OF THIS.
BLOW
Kettle drum—
ANY BAD JUGGLER CAN PLAY THIS.
BOING
BOING
Castanets—
CLICKETY CLICKETY CRUNCH
OW! MY POOR SOFT NOSE.
Glockenspiel—
OOYAH!
THWACK!
THWACK

THE MENACING WAY!
Piano—
YOOWL! MY DELICATE FINGERS!
WONDERED WHAT THIS WAS HOLDING UP.
SNATCH
THUD
SLAM
BITE
PYOING
Harp—
Alpenhorn—
PARP!
MUMSIE!
WALTER'S HOUSE
Trombone—
THIS DOESN'T SOUND LIKE THE TUNE I'M PLAYING.
THAT'S BECAUSE IT ISN'T.
TUG
TUG
Double bass—
GREAT SOUND, THIS!
SCREECH
TWANG

IN THE BEST POSSIBLE TASTE
CINEMA
"THE THING" IT'S HORRIBLE
PAY HERE
COO! SMASHING FILM, EH, LADS?
YES!
NOT HALF!
HOW COMMON!
FANCY GOING TO THE CINEMA!
AND TO WATCH A HORROR FILM, TOO!
BUT WE KNOW MENACES HAVE AWFULLY BAD TASTE, DON'T WE, CHUMS?
OH, YES! HO! HO!
WE'LL SOON FIX THOSE SOFTIES!
TRY SOME OF THIS!
GLUG!
GLUG!
GULG!
CASTOR OIL
YEUCH!
UGGHHH!
GLUG!
IT'S THE SOFTIES WHO HAVE THE "BAD TASTE" NOW!

HEY! LOOK AT THIS!
TODAY AT THE TOWN HALL! CULTURE CONTEST— £100 PRIZES FOR WINNING ENTRIES!
COME ON, GANG— WE'LL SING THEM OUR MENACING SONG!
ONLY ENTRIES IN GOOD TASTE ALLOWED.
HARD LUCK, YOU CADS.
WE'LL GIVE THEM CULTURE OK! SEE YOU BACK HERE IN FIVE MINUTES.
DADS' EVENING SUITS
HO! HO! LOOK AT THE SOFTIES!
SORRY, PAL! YOU'RE WRONG! TAKE THAT!
INSIDE THE TOWN HALL—
WALTER WINS A PRIZE FOR HIS POEM "THE LITTLE BIRDIES", AND NOW WE HAVE A LATE ENTRY—
—THE MENACING ENSEMBLE!
CRASH!
SCRAPE!
PARP!
HOWL!
WAIL!
SCREECH!
I'VE RECORDED YOUR WONDERFUL MUSIC! IT'S JUST WHAT I WAS NEEDING!
HOW DREADFUL!
AT THE LOCAL FAIRGROUND—
GHOST TRAIN
I NEEDED SOME NEW SOUND EFFECTS FOR THE "GHOST TRAIN" AT MY FAIRGROUND"!
GHOST TRAIN
PERFECT! IT SOUNDS REALLY HORRIBLE! THERE'S A FIVER!
IT'S THE MENACES WHO HAVE THE GOOD TASTE NOW! SLURP!
CHEW!
CHOMP!
BAH!

THE BEANO
MERRY CHRISTMAS MENACES!
No. 2527 DECEMBER 22nd, 1990.
EVERY THURSDAY
26p
DENNIS the MENACE and GNASHER
SING ALONG TO THE TUNE OF "GOOD KING WENCESLAS".
GOOD OLD DENNIS ONCE LOOKED IN, ON A FEAST FOR WALTER!
TEE-HEE! I'LL EAT THIS ALL MYSELF!
"SHARE WITH ME, YOU WEEDY SAP, OR YOUR FACE I'LL ALTER!"
WHAMPER!
MOAN!
TURN TO THE BACK COVER, MENACES!

DENNIS the MENACE and GNASHER
"BRING ME TURKEY, BRING ME SPUDS, PEAS, SPROUTS AND TOMATAS. WHILE YOU'RE AT IT, GIVE'S A FEW OF THESE CHIPOLATAS!"
LOUDLY HOWLED THE SOFTY BOY, "YOU'RE SO MEAN AND CRUEL". DENNIS MEANWHILE STUFFED HIS EARS FULL OF COTTON WOO-OO-OOL!
PLUCK
HOWL!
VERY SOON HE HAD A PLATE PILED UP LIKE A MOUNTAIN, MEANWHILE WALTER LOUDLY SOBBED— TEARS WELLED LIKE A FOU-OUNTAIN!
SOB!
SOB!
SLURP!
"HITHER, GNASHER, STAND BY ME, BRING OUR GIFT FOR WATTIE. WE MUST STOP HIS DREADFUL DIN, OR I'LL GO QUITE POTTY!"
CHOMP!
FOR WALTER
LEAP
WALTER RIPPED THE WRAPPING OFF. "OO! A LOVELY DOLLY."
CHOMP! CHEW!
THEN HE SQUEEZED HIS PREZZIE TIGHT— WHAT AN ACT OF FO-OLLY!
HOWL!
HOPE YOU GET ALL THE PRESENTS YOU WANT, READERS!
GNAPPY GRRISTMAS!
SQUIRT
HUG
SQUEEZE

THE Christmas BEANO
No. 2319 DECEMBER 27th, 1986.
EVERY THURSDAY
18p
I.R. 26p (inc. VAT)
DENNIS the MENACE and GNASHER
ON THE FIRST DAY OF CHRISTMAS THE MENACE GAVE TO ME...
... A PARSNIP FROM A SPARE SKI!
TWANG!
SPLUTCH!
ON THE SECOND DAY OF CHRISTMAS THE MENACE GAVE TO ME...
KNITTED BY BERTIE FOR DENNIS
UNWANTED CHRISTMAS PRESENT
...TWO HURTLED GLOVES...
...AND A PARSNIP FROM A SPARE SKI!
ON THE THIRD DAY OF CHRISTMAS THAT MENACE GAVE TO ME...
...THREE DRENCHED MEN...
...TWO HURTLED GLOVES...
...AND A PARSNIP FROM A SPARE SKI!
COMPLAINTS ABOUT DENNIS'S WATER PISTOL
MORE ON BACK PAGE

DENNIS the MENACE
AND GNASHER
CONTINUED FROM FRONT PAGE
FOUR CRAWLING BUGS...
...THREE DRENCHED MEN...
...TWO HURTLED GLOVES...
ON THE FOURTH DAY OF CHRISTMAS THAT MENACE GAVE TO ME...
FROM DENNIS
FROM DENNIS
...AND A PARSNIP FROM A SPARE SKI!
ON THE FIFTH DAY OF CHRISTMAS THAT MENACE GAVE TO ME...
NERVOUS REX
...FIVE CO-OLD THINGS...
...FOUR CRAWLING BUGS...
...THREE DRENCHED MEN...
...TWO HURTLED GLOVES...
SPLAT!
SPLAT!
SPLAT!
GNEE! GNEE!
...AND A PARSNIP FROM A SPARE SKI!
ON THE SIXTH DAY OF CHRISTMAS THAT MENACE GAVE TO ME...
DENNIS'S GRAN
TUG
...SIX BEASTS A-BRAYING...
...FIVE CO-OLD THINGS...
...FOUR CRAWLING BUGS...
...THREE DRENCHED MEN...
BRAY!
TUG
...TWO HURTLED GLOVES...
BRAY!
...AND A PARSNIP FROM A SPARE SKI!
ON THE SEVENTH DAY OF CHRISTMAS MY FATHER GAVE TO ME...
HAR! HAR!
... SOMETHING I'D RATHER NOT SING ABOUT.
SNIGGER!
TEE! HEE!
SORE!
FLY SPRAY

THE BEANO
MERRY GRRRISTMAS!
No. 2475 DECEMBER 23rd, 1989
EVERY THURSDAY
24p
I.R. 37p (Inc. VAT)
DENNIS the MENACE and GNASHER
YOU'D BETTER WATCH OUT, KEEP OPEN ONE EYE, THERE'S DANGER ABOUT, I'M TELLING YOU WHY— GNASHER CLAWS IS COMING TO TOWN!
FILE!
NOW TURN TO THE BACK PAGE.

DENNIS and GNASHER
HE'S MAKING A LIST AND CHECKING IT TWICE. HE'S WANTING TO SCRATCH ANY BOYS THAT ARE NICE. GNASHER CLAWS IS COMING TO TOWN.
BERTIE BLENKINSOP
NERVOUS REX
DUDLEY NIGHTSHIRT
SPOTTY PERKINS
WALTER
YEEOWP!
JAB
HE'LL JAB YOU WHEN YOU'RE SLEEPING. HE'LL GOUGE WHEN YOU'RE AWAKE. HE HATES YOU WHEN YOU'VE BEEN EXTRA GOOD— SO BE RUDE FOR GOODNESS SAKE!
SUM BOOK 100 100
EEK!
GOUGE
RAZZ!
RAZZ!
HO-HO-HO!
YOU'D BETTER WATCH OUT. YOU'D BETTER BEWARE. PLEASE DON'T BE A LOUT, 'COS LOOK OVER THERE— SANTA CLAUS IS COMING TO TOWN!
ULP!
I'D BETTER WATCH OUT, IF I WANT SOME TOYS. 'COS THAT FELLOW CLAUS, GIVES NOTHING TO BOYS WHO CAUSE A LOT OF TROUBLE IN TOWN!
HO-HO-HO!
PLOP!

DESPERATE DAN-SING
AH'M TAKIN' SINGIN' LESSONS.
FIRST, YOU MUST FILL YOUR LUNGS WITH AIR. TAKE A DEEP BREATH.
DIPLOMA
SURE THING, MA'AM.
But —
SUCK!
RIP!
SHRIEK! STOP!
DRAG!

One dressing later —
LET ME HEAR YOU RUN UP THE SCALE.
DOH-RAY-
POP!
TINKLE!
MEEEEEEEE!
TINKLE!
CRACK!
CRACK!
TINKLE!
TINKLE!
CRACK!
YIKES! MY POOR EARS!
NOW I'LL TRY THE HIGH NOTES.
GULP!
CRACK!
I'VE GONE DEAF — AND BLIND!

OOOOHHHH!
SHAKE!
SLAM!
OOOOOO-HHHHH!
OO-ER!
HOWL!
WHAT'S THAT?

THAT'S ENOUGH FOR TODAY.
MISS D. NOTE
AH THINK AH'VE LEARNED A LOT, MA'AM!
Back home —
BATH ROOM
IS UNCLE DAN LEARNING TO BE AN OPERA STAR, AUNTIE?
NO, DANNY.
HE JEST WANTS TO SOUND BETTER WHEN HE'S SINGING IN THE BATH.
FOAM-FOAM ON THE RANGE!

WHAT A BRASSNECK
BRASS BAND COMPETITION TODAY
MUST ENTER THAT.
ONE SMALL PROBLEM...
...WE DON'T HAVE ANY BRASS INSTRUMENTS!
NOT TO WORRY!
I'M VERY PROUD OF MY BRASS COLLECTION.
THESE WILL DO NICELY!
SOME STRINGS ON THIS...
...AND A COVER FOR THIS...
...AND WE'VE GOT A BRASS BAND!
TOOT!

Soon–
CAN'T LET THEM REACH THE CONTEST–THEY'RE SURE TO WIN!
TAA-RA-RAA!
DENNIS'S DAD
BRASS BAND CONCERT THAT WAY.
THANKS, FRIEND.
THAT CHAP LOOKS A BIT FAMILIAR!
HEH-HEH! THAT SHOULD FIX THEM!
TAA-RAA!
BEANOTOWN
MARSH
At the contest–
OH, DEAR! IT'S THEM!
SOFTIES
WE'RE OFF TO FETCH COTTON WOOL FOR OUR EARS, SO WE CAN'T HEAR THE AWFUL DIN THEY'RE BOUND TO MAKE!
HEH-HEH! THEY'VE LEFT THEIR INSTRUMENTS!
Later–
FIRST, WE HAVE THE SOFTIES' BAND.
BRASS BAND CONTEST
TROMBONE FILLED WITH SOAP LIQUID
SNEEZING POWDER
STINK BOMBS
ACHOO! ACHOO! ACHOO!
AGH! I'VE GOT SOAP IN MY EYES!
HAR-HAR! THAT'S THEM OUT OF THE WAY!
SWOON
THE SOFTIES ARE IN NO STATE TO CONTINUE–THE MENACES ARE THE ONLY CONTESTANTS LEFT!
HOLD ON, THERE!
ERK! DAD!
SNATCH
Later–
"POLISHING" UP YOUR ACT, EH?
BAH! OUR BAND'S BEEN BANNED!
POLISH

THE
The Christmas BEANO
BEANO
No. 2736 DECEMBER 24th 1994
EVERY THURSDAY 38p
Dennis the Menace and GNASHER
Christmas Song.
Sung to the tune of
'I Saw Three Ships'.
I SAW THREE SOFTIES PRANCING BY,
ON CHRISTMAS DAY, ON CHRISTMAS DAY.
'TWAS THEN I TOOK A MIGHTY SHY,
ON CHRISTMAS DAY IN THE MORNING.
ROLL
MY SNOWBALL LANDED ON THESE THREE,
ON CHRISTMAS DAY, ON CHRISTMAS DAY.
MUCH TO ME AND GNASHER'S GLEE,
ON CHRISTMAS DAY IN THE MORNING.
ROLL
ROLL
RUMBLE
TUMBLE
THE SNOWBALL THEN BEGAN TO ROLL,
ON CHRISTMAS DAY, ON CHRISTMAS DAY.
AND PICKED UP DAD OUT FOR A STROLL,
ON CHRISTMAS DAY IN THE MORNING.
ROLL
FLATTEN

THE BALL OF SNOW BEGAN TO SLOW,
ON CHRISTMAS DAY, ON CHRISTMAS DAY.
SO WE LEAPT ON IT TO MAKE IT GO,
ON CHRISTMAS DAY IN THE MORNING.
ZOOM
WE ROLLED IT THROUGH A BIG HOTEL,
ON CHRISTMAS DAY, ON CHRISTMAS DAY.
AND PICKED UP LOADS OF FOOD AS WELL,
ON CHRISTMAS DAY IN THE MORNING.
OLD SANTA THEN CAME INTO VIEW,
ON CHRISTMAS DAY, ON CHRISTMAS DAY.
SO MR CLAUS WAS ROLLED ON TOO,
ON CHRISTMAS DAY IN THE MORNING.
HOTEL EXIT
ROLL
CRASH!
XMAS PRESSIES
BUT THEN THINGS THEY WENT SLIGHTLY WRONG,
ON CHRISTMAS DAY, ON CHRISTMAS DAY.
WE SMELLED A LOVELY CURRY PONG,
ON CHRISTMAS DAY IN THE MORNING.
ROLL
CURRY
PONG
NIFF

TWAS FATTY WITH A VINDALOO,
ON CHRISTMAS DAY, ON CHRISTMAS DAY.
AND O'ER THE SNOWBALL SAUCE THEN FLEW,
ON CHRISTMAS DAY IN THE MORNING.
CRUMP
SPLISH
THUD
THE SNOWBALL MELTED CLEAN AWAY,
ON CHRISTMAS DAY, ON CHRISTMAS DAY.
TO ME AND GNASHER'S GREAT DISMAY,
ON CHRISTMAS DAY IN THE MORNING.
HSSSSS
HSSSS
A HAPPY ENDING TO THIS RHYME,
ON CHRISTMAS DAY, ON CHRISTMAS DAY.
WHEN SANTA YELLED OUT, "PARTY TIME!"
ON CHRISTMAS DAY IN THE MORNING.
CHOC CAT
CHOMP

A MENACE SONG FOR CHRISTMAS
READY BOYS?
Carols
Carols
OO! I LOVE CHRISTMAS CAROLS!
SOFTY WALTER
WE
GNISH
YOU A
MERRY
GNISH GNASH—
WE
GNISH
YOU A MERRY
GNISH GNASH—
WE
GNISH
YOU A MERRY
GNISH GNASH—
—AND A HAPPY
STAND BY FOR THE BIG FINALE, READERS.
GNOOOOOOOOOO....
....PAIR OF SPECS!
READER'S VOICE
"AND A HAPPY NEW PAIR OF SPECS"—I DIDN'T THINK THOSE WERE THE WORDS! HO-HO-HO!
CRACK
CRACK

FACE THE MUSIC
All is peaceful in Beanotown...
ZZZZ!
ZZZ!
ZZ
ZZZZ!
ZZZZ!
ZZZZ!
SUDDENLY-
EEK!
HORRIBLE DIN
SQUAWK!
YIKES!
BAWL!
WOOF!
SCREECH!
AWFUL RACKET!
PESKY "DENNIS AND THE DINMAKERS" DISTURBING THE PEACE!
SHAKE
TREMBLE
BOOM DA BOOM!
OUR LULLABY CHOIR IS MUCH MORE SOOTHING.
SOFTIES
SO-
"GOLDEN SLUMBERS KISS YOUR EYES..."
ZZZZ!
ZZZ!
HMM! THAT GIVES ME AN IDEA!

DO YOU DO REQUESTS? HOW ABOUT "HUSH-A-BYE BABY"?
OO! WE LIKE THAT ONE!
SONG SHEET
"HUSH-A-BYE BABY, ON THE TREE TOP..."
GUARD DOG
TIPTOE
TIPTOE
SNORE!
GRUNT!
HEH-HEH! WE'RE ON THE TREE TOP NOW — COLLECTING CONKERS!
SNORE!
PLUCK!
SOON—
KNOW ANY MORE LULLABYS?
PUBLIC PARK
BUT OF COURSE!
"GO TO SLEEP! GO TO SLEEP! FOR THE SANDMAN IS COMING..."
SONG BOOK
SONG BOOK
"GO TO SLEEP! GO TO SLEEP! FOR THE SANDMAN IS COMING..."
Z-Z-Z!
TIPTOE
GOOD! THAT GRUMPY PARKIE'S ASLEEP...
Z-Z-Z!
YAH! SAPS! WE JUST USED YOU TO GET CONKERS AND OUR BALL BACK!
GNAHA-HA!
"HUSH, LITTLE BABY, DON'T YOU CRY..."
SWOOSH!
EEK!
SPLUTTER!
SNORE!
HAR-HAR! KNEW THAT WINDOW CLEANER WOULD FALL ASLEEP IN HIS CRADLE!
GURR!
GNASH!

TAP! TAP!
TINKLE!
PLONK!
TWANG!
BOOM!
BANGA!
BOOM!
SQUEAK!
TOOT!
BANG!
DOINK!
POUND!
DINK!
BLART!
BOING!
BOOMEDY!
PEEP!
BOOM!
DING!
BONG!
CLAP!
SCREECH!
BOOM!
BOOMEDY!
BOOM!
WHY DID THE FOOTBALLER WEAR FLIPPERS?
BECAUSE HE WAS IN THE FIRST TEAM POOL!
ORCHESTRATED RIOT
THE VISITING MUSIC TEACHER IS COMING TO SCHOOL!
BASH STREET SCHOOL
MUSIC TEACHER
PARP
RUMBLE
In class IIB.
I'M GOING TO LET YOU ALL TRY OUT VARIOUS INSTRUMENTS — TO SEE WHA
YOU'RE GOOD AT!
MUSICAL INSTRUMENTS
PULL
TRUNDLE
OH! NOT NOW!
WAA!
PARP!
I'D QUITE LIKE TO PLAY THIS!
BUT I'M NOT SURE IF MY MOUTH IS BIG ENOUGH!
MAYBE NOT — BUT YOU'VE GOT A VERY USEFUL HARD HEAD!
. . . YOU ARE DISTURBING DANNY'S DRUMMING!
WAP
THUNK
WHAT A WONDERFUL SOUND YOU ARE GETTING FROM THAT BIG DRUM!
OO . . . BAH . . . DOOM!
Then —
RIP OPEN
HEH-HEH! IT WAS CUTHBERT INSIDE IT!
WE GIVE UP! NONE O
THESE INSTRUMENTS A
AT ALL SUITED TO YOU LOT!
WOW! MY HEAD!
DAZED
TWANG! DOINK! BONG! CLAP! POUND! PEEP! SQUEAK! BOING! BLART!

WHAT DO YOU GET IF YOU CROSS A DOG WITH A PHONE?
A GOLDEN RECEIVER!
OOH!
WAH!
COO!
DIVE
LEAP
MUSICAL INSTRUMENTS
EH? WHAT'S ALL THIS?
WE BOTH WANT TO PLAY THIS TROMBONE!
PULL
TUG
YEAH!
HOW NICE! THEY'RE BOTH PLAYING IT!
PARP
BADOOING
WHACK
I WANT TO PLAY THIS! ALL THE BLACK KEYS ARE MADE OF LIQUORICE!
KEYBOARD
AND YOU DON'T REALLY NEED THEM TO PLAY IT!
SCOOP
But —
DON'T SPIT THESE OUT . . .
PING
PHOO
BAH! NOT MADE OF LIQUORICE AFTER ALL! HUH!
YES! I AGREE!
BUT WE MIGHT BE ABLE TO USE THESE!
HOW INTERESTING!
THIS IS SOMEWHERE SAFE TO HAVE OUR CUP OF TEA!
ZAP
SQUASH
BOUNCE
TWANG
CLUNK
FLATTEN
TAP! TAP!
TINKLE!
PLONK!
TWANG!
BOOM!
BANGA!
BOOM!
SQUEAK!
TOOT!
BANG!
DOINK!
POUND!
DINK!
BLART!
BOING!
BOOMEDY!
PEEP!
BOOM!
DING!
BONG!
CLAP!
SCREECH!
BOOM!
BOOMEDY!
BOOM!
DINK! PLONK! TOOT! SCREECH! TWANG! DOINK! BONG! CLAP! POUND!

HERBERT VON BING BONG CONDUCTS...
THE MENACE ORCHESTRA
MUFFLED YELLS FOR HELP
BLOOP!
BLOOP!
PUFF BLOW
SOAPY LIQUID
PLINK
PLONK
TWANNNNG
AMMO
PLINK PLONK
BACH
VERDI
MOZART
SLAP!
SPIN
EAT AT JOE'S CAFE
LEAP
THROW
PLINK!
PLONK!
PLINK!
PLONK!
HERBERT VON BING BONG

POP!
POP!
POP!
THWAP!
BADOING!
RUMBLE
POP
BOING
TING -A- LING!
WHAP!
SILENCE
BARLEY
SPLAT!
STUFF
TWANG!
CHOP!
CHOP!
PEELED POTATOES
FOR HALF-TIME CHIPS
SUCK!
SLURP!
DEEP FAT FRYER
SIZZLE!
RASHER'S TROUGH

The Beano Book is underway.
Underway, underway.
See the stars in joyful play.
Joyful play, joyful play.
You will chuckle I should say,
so read on right away!
SING TO THE TUNE OF "NYMPHS AND SHEPHERDS"

C'mon thunder those drums
let's thrash those guitars.
We'll raise the roof
'cos we're top Beano stars.
That's all for now,
doncha dare shed a tear.
Rock along with this band
every week of the year.
IF Y' WANT MORE LAUGHS WITH THE CHARACTERS IN THIS BOOK ...
TUNE NTO

THE
ON SALE EVERY THURSDAY
BEANO

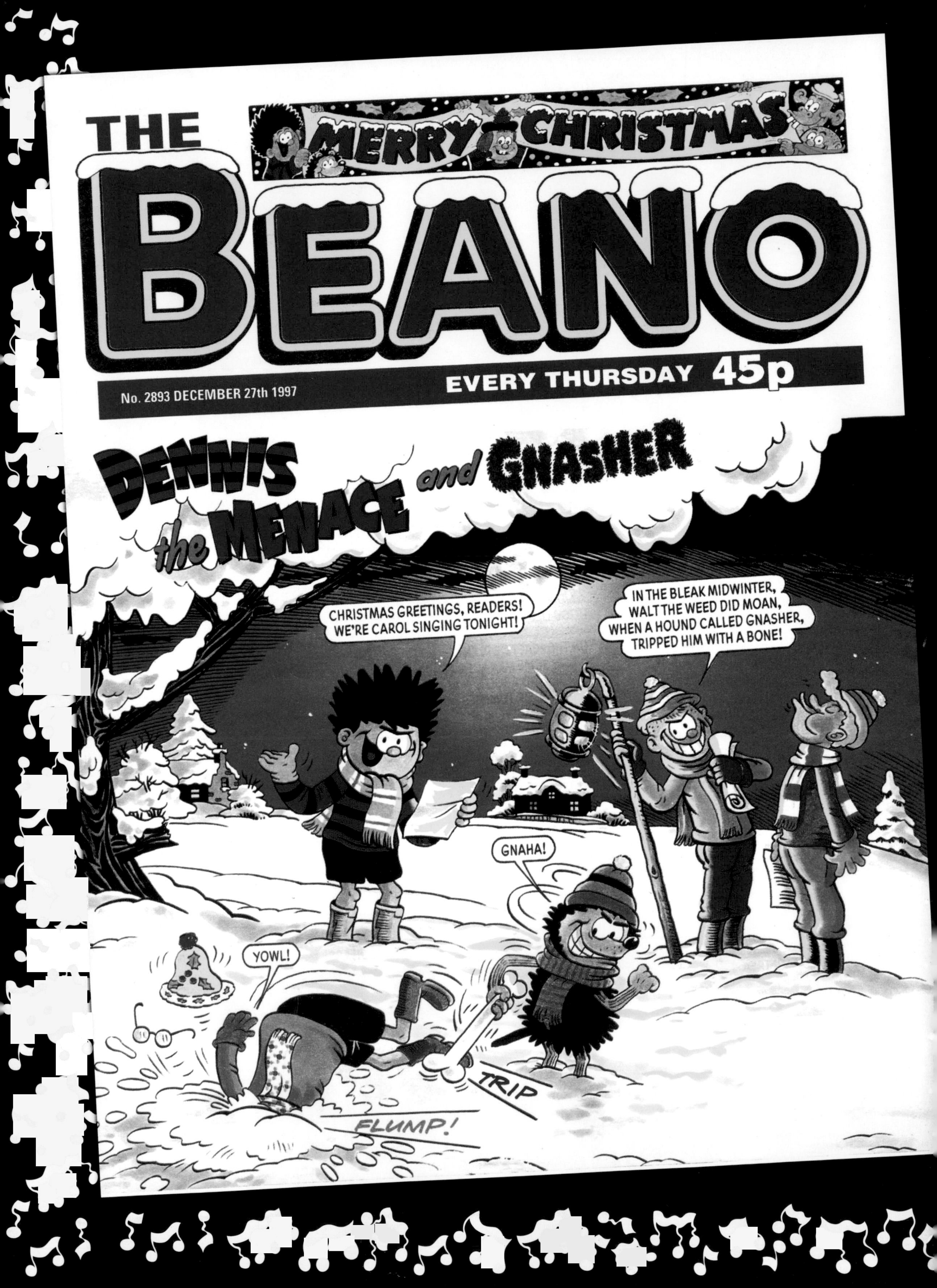
MERRY CHRISTMAS
THE BEANO
EVERY THURSDAY 45p
No. 2893 DECEMBER 27th 1997
DENNIS the MENACE and GNASHER
CHRISTMAS GREETINGS, READERS! WE'RE CAROL SINGING TONIGHT!
IN THE BLEAK MIDWINTER, WALT THE WEED DID MOAN, WHEN A HOUND CALLED GNASHER, TRIPPED HIM WITH A BONE!
GNAHA!
YOWL!
TRIP
FLUMP!

Have a Happy Christmas and an even —
WHILE BERTIE WASHED HIS SOCKS BY NIGHT AND HUNG THEM ON THE LINE,
A BOY CALLED DENNIS TOOK THEM DOWN, AND GAVE THEM TO HIS SWINE!
STOMP
STOMP
BAH! NO MONEY — ONLY SMELLY SOCKS!
PONG!
NIFF!
THERE ARE OUR DADS COMING HOME WITH THE CHRISTMAS SHOPPING!
HUH! THEY'RE TOO MEAN TO GIVE US ANY MONEY, BUT WE'LL GIVE THEM A CAROL ANYWAY!
PRANG YOUR DAD WITH BOUGHS OF HOLLY! TRA-LA-LA-LA-LA!
YOU CAN BET THEY WON'T BE JOLLY! TRA-LA-LA-LA-LA!
OW!
EEK!
WAH!
WHACK!
WHACK!
THWACK!
GNEE-HEE!
WE'RE OUTSIDE YOUR GRANNY'S HOUSE NOW, DENNIS!
SHARPEN YOUR VOCAL CHORDS, PALS! GRANNY'S BOUND TO GIVE US SOME FESTIVE CHEER!
GOOD OLD GRANNY ONCE LOOKED OUT, ON THE FEAST OF PLENTY. SAW SOME MENACES ROUND ABOUT, WITH THEIR TUMMIES EMPTY!
GNOOOOO!
SO SHE BROUGHT US OUT SOME EATS, THOUGH THE WIND WAS CRUEL. GRAN'S PLUM PUDDINGS CAN'T BE BEAT, THEY'RE SUPER WINTER FU-U-EL!
LIFT!
BAH! THOSE PESTS HAVE WOKEN ME UP!
ALL YOU GET FROM ME ARE THESE STALE PLUM PUDS I MADE IN 1932!
EEK! LET'S RETREAT!
WHEEE
WAH!
Later...
WE'VE BROUGHT OUR GUITARS OUT TO ADD HARMONY!
AFTER THREE, PALS. ONE, TWO, THREE . . .

WE'RE FOUR MENACES WE ARE, STRUMMING CAROLS ON OUR GUITARS, GIVE US GRUB AND GIVE US MONEY, THEN WE'LL TRAVEL AFAR!
CLICK!
CLICK
TWANG
YOU CAN SING THERE ALL NIGHT IF YOU WANT! WE'RE ALL WEARING EAR-PLUGS!
YES, WE WERE WARNED YOU WERE COMING!
BAH!
A WASTE OF GOOD MUSIC!
HMM . . . THAT BELFRY GIVES ME AN IDEA. OUR VOICES WILL SOUND BETTER FROM THAT HEIGHT! HAR-HAR!
AHA! AS I THOUGHT THE SOFTIES! THERE'S ONLY ONE CAROL WE CAN SING!
DING-DONG! MENACING ON HIGH! THE BELLS ARE GAILY RINGING!
ZOOM
WHEE
THE SOFTIES UNHAPPILY REPLY, WHEN THEIR HEADS ARE STINGING!
YOWL!
OUCH!
HOWL!
HERE ARE SOME PRESSIES FOR YOUR CAROL SINGING!
THROW
YAHOO! AT LEAST SANTA LIKES OUR VOICES!
CHORTLE!
WOW! SPECIAL AMERICAN BASEBALL CAPS WITH MOUTH GUARDS!
CLICK!
HAW-HAW! NOW PERHAPS WE'LL HAVE A SILENT NIGHT! MERRY CHRISTMAS, EVERYBODY!
MUMBLE!
MURFLE!
TUG!

PIGS MIGHT PLAY
I'M A VERY MUSICAL PIG.
GET OUT OF MY PIANO SHOP! WE DON'T SERVE PIGS.
PIANOS FOR SALE
OINKWAH!
FRUITERE
NEVER MIND . . .
SNATCH
BLOW
. . . I'LL JUST BLOW OUT THE INSIDE . . .
. . . MAKE A FEW TUSK HOLES . . .
POP!
POP!
. . . AND I HAVE A FLUTE!
PHEEP!
I KNOW THAT TUNE!
OH! WHEN THE PIGS! OH! WHEN THE PIGS COME SNORTING IN!
VERY GOOD!
Soon—
THANK YOU!
NO MONEY FOR ME, EH?
SNATCH
HERE'S SOMETHING A REAL FLUTE IS NO USE FOR.
THROW
SKIP
GLUB! CAN'T SEE.
I'M GOING TO BUY A MUCH BETTER INSTRUMENT NOW..
So—
I'LL HAVE ALL YOUR STOCK.
MARROWS
PERFECT!

DENNIS and the DINMAKE
OH, WE WANNA MAKE A NOISE, YEAH, WE WANNA MAKE A DIN. BETTER WATCH YOUR CD PLAYER, IF YOU GIVE OUR SONGS A SPIN.
OH, WE WANNA MAKE A NOISE, YEAH, WE WANNA MAKE A DIN. IF YOU TELL US TO BE QUIET, WE WILL DUMP YOU IN A BIN.
BOOM -DA BOOM
ARCTIC
CRACK
CRACK
BOOM
CRACK
CRACK
SOME PEOPLE YELLED, "YOU'RE TRAGIC!" WHICH WASN'T VERY NICE. THEY SENT US TO THE ARCTIC BUT OUR PLAYING CRACKED THE ICE.

UNPLUGGED
THEY'RE UNPLUGGED ALL RIGHT— THEY WOULDN'T LET ME PLAY!
WE PLAYED OUR SONGS ON TELLY BUT WE SHATTERED VIEWERS SCREENS. THEY PELTED US WITH JELLY, TILL GNASHER RIPPED THEIRJEANS.
JELLY
FIZZ
RIP
JELLY
OH, WE WANNA MAKE A NOISE, YEAH, WE WANNA MAKE A DIN. GOOD OL' GNASHER HIT A HIGH NOTE WHEN HE SAT UPON A PIN.
EEEYOW!

GNURSERY RHYMES

SCREAM!

PAT-A-CAKE, PAT-A-CAKE,
DEAR OLD MUM.
BAKE ME A CAKE, GO ON,
BE A CHUM.
PAT IT AND PRICK IT AND
PILE ON THICK CREAM.
I'LL GIVE IT TO WALTER
WHO'S LIKELY TO SCREAM.

FLOUR

SIMPLE SIMON MET A PIE MAN
GOING TO THE FAIR.
SAID SIMPLE SIMON TO THE PIE MAN,
"LET ME TASTE YOUR WARE."
SAID THE PIE MAN TO SIMPLE SIMON,
"THE TRADE'S BEEN REALLY BUZZIN'!
PIE FACE BOUGHT UP ALL MY PIES–
HE'S SCOFFED AROUND EIGHT DOZEN!"

DENNIS HAD A LITTLE PIG,
IT'S SKIN WAS ROUGH AND PINK.
IT USED TO GUZZLE FOOD ALL DAY-
MY GOODNESS, WHAT A STINK!
BURP!
HEY DIDDLE DIDDLE THE CAT AND
THE FIDDLE,
THE DOG JUMPED OVER THE GATE.
THE LITTLE BOY LAUGHED TO SEE
SUCH FUN,
TILL THE CAT GOT REVENGE ON
HIS MATE.
WALTER HAD A LITTLE LAMB,
HE BOUGHT THE BEAST FROM MARY.
HE SHOWED IT TO HIS CHUMMY REX,
WHO FOUND IT RATHER SCARY.
OLD MOTHER HUBBARD WENT TO THE
CUPBOARD,
TO GET HER POOR DOGGIE A BONE.
BUT THE OLD GIRL LOOKED BEATEN,
'COS GNASHER HAD EATEN
HER DOG'S GRUB AND ALSO HER OWN!

Fun at Your Convenience
HUH? EVEN I KNOW THESE ARE WEIRD NOISES TO COME FROM A TOILET.
BAFFLED SCRATCH!
PAARP! TOOT! PEEP!
Toilets
ENGAGED
PUFF! BLAST!
TEECH
MILK
OO-ER! EVEN CURRIED PRUNES DON'T DO THAT TO ME.
BLARE! RAASP! HONK!
POOT! BOOM!
Toilets
FATTY'S LUNCH TROUGH
!
LOO AND BEHOLD! SOMETHING ODD'S GOING ON IN THERE.
TINKLE! PLINKLE! PHRRPT!
Toilets
ENGAGED

PAAARP! TINKLE! BLARE! BOOMEDY-BOOM!
CREAK
BOOM!
HOOT! TOOT! HONK!
SQUEAK! QUONK! BLAART!
RAASP! FRRT!
TINKLE! DING!
PUFF!
CHING!
SWING!
THAT'S THE ONLY PLACE TEACHER WILL LET 'ERBERT PRACTISE!

TAP! TAP!
TINKLE!
PLONK!
TWANG!
BOOM!
BANGA!
BOOM!
SQUEAK!
TOOT!
BANG!
DOINK!
POUND!
DINK!
BLART!
BOING!
BOOMEDY!
PEEP!
BOOM!
DING!
BONG!
CLAP!
SCREECH!
BOOM!
BOOMEDY!
BOOM!
BUSK TILL DUSK
WAH!
HOWL!
DENNIS IS "BUSKING"
TA!
SCREECH!
TA!
AWFUL!
GRRRGNASH!
LOVELY! HAVE LOTS OF MONEY!
GEE! TA!
GNASH!
TA!
WHAT'S THIS SOFT NIT UP TO?
THIS WAY, CHAPPIES!
TRUST THE SOFTY!
GNEH?
CLUMP
TA!
LOVELY RENDERING OF "AVE MARIA"
BEAUTIFUL! FANTASTIC!
HUH! NO-ONE'S GOT ANY MUSICAL TASTE AROUND HERE!
TWANG! DOINK! BONG! CLAP! POUND! PEEP! SQUEAK! BOING! BLART!

YOU'LL BE A STAR, WALTER!
RECORD PRODUCER
DO YOU REALLY THINK SO? TWITTER!
CONTRACT
YEUCH!
RECORDING STUDIO
COME ON, GNASHER—LET'S DO SOME MENACING HERE!
DO YOU HAVE A PASS?
YES—THIS IS IT!
ULP!
PASS
CONTROL ROOM
RECORDING IN PROGRESS
LA-LA!
READY, GNASHER?
WAAH!
GNWAH!
HIGH-PITCHED SCREAM!
GOLDEN DISC AWARDS
TINKLE!
CRASH!
FIZZ!
EH?
THROB
THROB
THROB
THROB
SPLUT! FIZZ!
ICE
FOR EAR-ACHE
ICE PACK
BILL FOR £1000
BROKEN GLASS
PAY UP—OR ELSE!
CONTRACT
SO—
GIVE GENEROUSLY—ONLY £999.73 TO GO!
RATTLE!
TRYING TO SING SWEETLY
SCREECH!
BOOM-DA-BOOM!
TAP! TAP!
TINKLE!
PLONK!
TWANG!
BOOM!
BANGA!
BOOM!
SQUEAK!
TOOT!
BANG!
DOINK!
POUND!
DINK!
BLART!
BOING!
BOOMEDY!
PEEP!
BOOM!
DING!
BONG!
CLAP!
SCREECH!
BOOM!
BOOMEDY!
BOOM!
DINK! PLONK! TOOT! SCREECH! TWANG! DOINK! BONG! CLAP! POUND!

DENNIS
OUR GROUP NEVER QUITE MADE THE HIT PARADE!
PLENTY WORK FOR ME WITH DENNIS'S POP GROUP AROUND!
F. PAYNE GLAZIER
TINKLE!
TINKLE!
CRASH!
TINKLE!
CRASH!
YIKES! WE'LL STEER WELL CLEAR OF THAT RACKET!
WHO NEEDS A FOGHORN WITH THE DINMAKERS ABOARD?

DINMAKERS
H.M. PRISON
ERK! TOO NOISY OUT HERE!
WOW! THE DINMAKERS HAVE DRIVEN BACK THE ESCAPED PRISONERS!
FILM COMPANY
PERFECT! THEY REALLY MAKE THE PLACE SHAKE!
SAND BAGS
WHIRR!
RECORDING OF EARTHQUAKE SEQUENCE
BRAVO!
WELL DONE!
CLAP!
CLAP!
WE MAY NOT HAVE MADE THE HIT PARADE BUT WE CERTAINLY PICKED UP A FEW FANS!

Christmas
Singalon
THE
DINN
Dennis is King, the Dinmake
The Old Folks cringe, their
Dreams of Santa, dreams
Shaking the trees with Sa
Christmas time, presen
Snowballs zinging, hitt
With dogs by the fire a
A great time for Menac
A time for sledging,
A time for snowboa
We love laughter
Than swinging
a rafter.
Christmas
Rasher's b
With dog
A time fo
RASHER
RASHER

Sing to the tune of "Mistletoe and Wine".
ng,
ls are spinning.
ow,
below.
, so fine,
very time.
Valt on the tree,
ll that you see.
e for skating,
and Softy baiting.
what could be dafter,
streamers hung over
e, Granny's scoffed the wine,
ng — what a greedy swine.
ing higher at Walt on the tree,
oring in front of TV.

Bea: Que Sera, Sera
When I was just a little girl, I asked my brother
What will I be?
Will I be pretty?
Will I be rich?
Here's what he said to me...
NIGEL PARKINSON

BIFF!
KER-LONK!
WHAM
THUNK!
DON'T BE DAFT, BE DAFT!
I KNOW WHAT YOU'LL BE,
YOU'LL BE...
A MENACE
LIKE ME, LIKE ME!
QUE SERA, SERA!!
WHAT WILL BE
WILL BE!!

DENNIS and the DINMAKERS
MUSICAL MAYHEM
GARAGE
AIR GUITAR
FREE AIR
TWANG!
SPLUTCH!
CRASH!
BLAST!
BOING -DA- BOING!
OIL
TOOLS
OIL
OIL
TAP! TAP!
TINKLE!
PLONK!
TWANG!
BOOM!
BANGA!
BOOM!
SQUEAK!
TOOT!
BANG!
DOINK!
POUND!
DINK!
BLART!
BOING!
BOOMEDY!
PEEP!
BOOM!
DING!
BONG!
CLAP!
SCREECH!
BOOM!
BOOMEDY!
BOOM!
TWANG! DOINK! BONG! CLAP! POUND! PEEP! SQUEAK! BOING! BLART!

HAVE A MENACING CHRISTMAS!

THE BEANO

web site address www.beanotown.com

No.3154, December 28th 2002. Every Thursday 65p Canada $2.50

RETURN OF LITTLE PLUM INSIDE

SING ALONG WITH DENNIS AND FRIENDS AS THEY BRING YOU THEIR VERSIONS OF CHRISTMAS CAROLS

ABOMINABLE SNOWMAN!

DIABOLICAL SNOWMAN!

SNOWMAN!

WE THREE KIDS FROM BEANOTOWN ARE,
SEEKING SNOW WE TRAVEL AFAR,
FIELD AND FOUNTAIN, MOOR AND MOUNTAIN,
IN OUR COOL MENACE CAR.

O, CAR OF WONDER, WHAT A SIGHT.
GOT SOME SNOW AND PACKED IT TIGHT.
HOMEWARD FLYING, WE'RE JUST DYING,
TO GIVE SOME SAPS A DREADFUL FRIGHT.

Sing to the tune of "We Three Kings"

OPEN!

ZOOOOM!

THE FOOTHILLS OF THE HIMALAYAS

I SAW THREE DRIPS COME PRANCING BY
ON CHRISTMAS DAY, ON CHRISTMAS DAY,
I SAW THREE DRIPS COME PRANCING BY
ON CHRISTMAS DAY IN THE MORNING.
I GNASHED THREE DRIPS WITH UTMOST GLEE
ON CHRISTMAS DAY, ON CHRISTMAS DAY.
I GNASHED THREE DRIPS WITH UTMOST GLEE
ON CHRISTMAS DAY IN THE MORNING.
I CHASED THREE DRIPS RIGHT UP A TREE
ON CHRISTMAS DAY, ON CHRISTMAS DAY.
BUT THEN THEY TOOK REVENGE ON ME
ON CHRISTMAS DAY IN THE MORNING.
Sing to the tune of "I Saw Three Ships"
ABDOMINAL SNOWMAN!
ALL I WANT FOR CHRISTMAS IS MY TWO FRONT TEETH,
MY TWO FRONT TEETH, SEE MY TWO FRONT TEETH,
GEE, IF ONLY I COULD HAVE MY TWO FRONT TEETH,
THEN I'D HELP POOR GNASHER OUT AT CHRISTMAS.
Sing to the tune of "All I Want For Christmas Is My Two Front Teeth"
GNASHER
Happy Christmas x

ABNORMAL SNOWMAN!
PIG PONG MESSILY IN STY
GOOD HEAVENS THE SMELL IS MINGING.
PIG PONG, WOW THAT NIFF IS HIGH,
MY LUNCH UP IS BRINGING.
GROO-OO-OO-OO-OO OO
OO-OO-OO-OO-OO-OO-OO-
OO-OO-OO-OO-OO-OO-OO-
THIS GRAN DON'T WANT TO
SMELL THIS!
Sing to the tune of "Ding Dong Merrily On High"
HUMM!
GLOOP!
CHFF!
SLEIGH BELLS RING, ARE YOU LISTENING?
WE'RE IN SPAIN - SOMEONE'S MISSING.
WE'RE FEELING ALL RIGHT,
WE'VE GOT A CHEAP FLIGHT,
CHRISTMAS WITHOUT
DENNIS WONDERLAND.
Sing to the tune of "Winter Wonderland"

DENNIS and the DINMAKERS
MUSICAL MAYHEM
HIP HOP
OLD FOLK'S HOME
HIP REPLACEMENT GROUP HOP
GENTLE TWANGING
TAP! TAP!
SPIN!
SWISH!
WHEEEE!
BUMP!
THUD!
CLAP!
HOP!

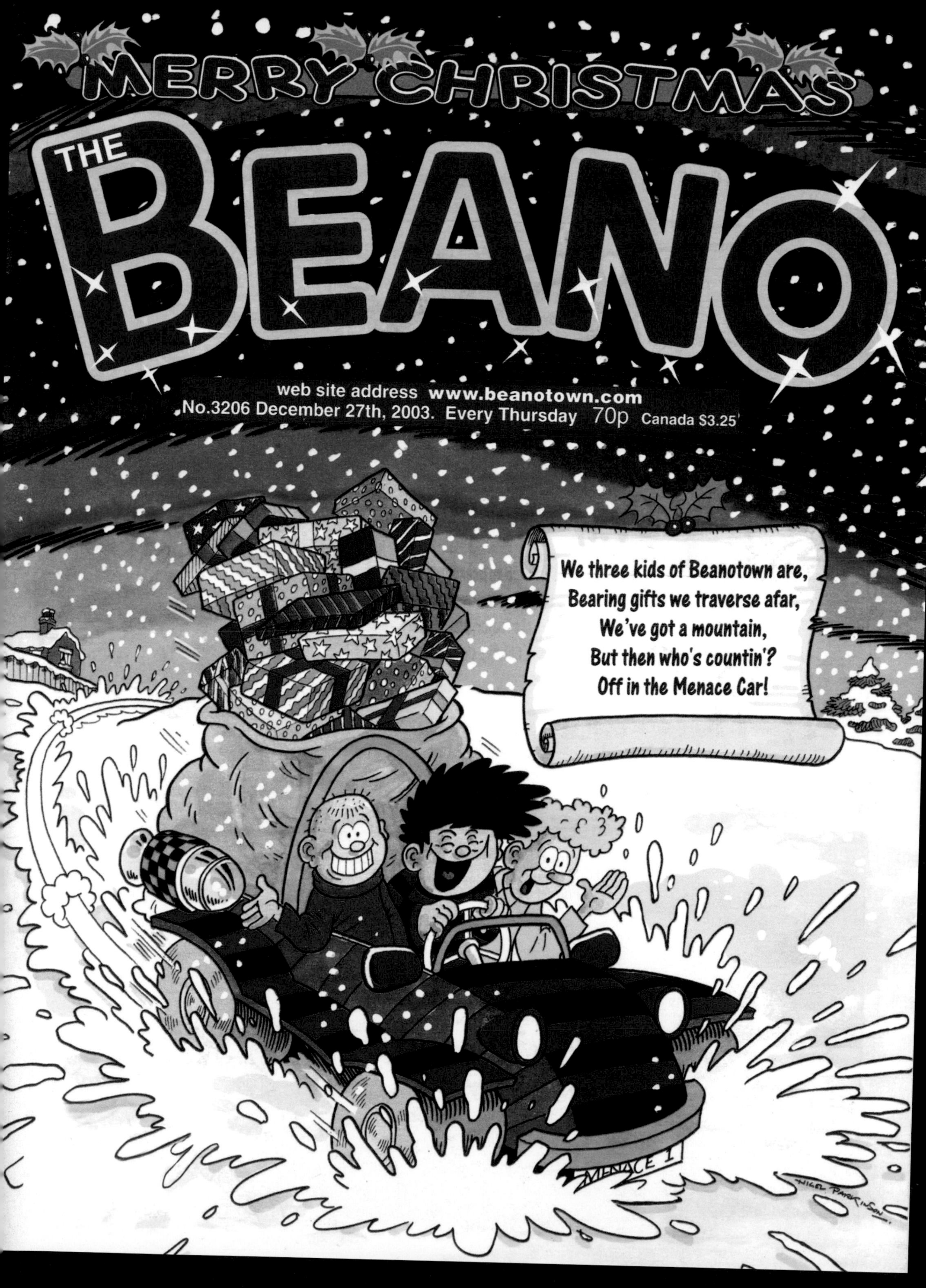

MERRY CHRISTMAS

THE BEANO

web site address www.beanotown.com
No.3206 December 27th, 2003. Every Thursday 70p Canada $3.25

We three kids of Beanotown are,
Bearing gifts we traverse afar,
We've got a mountain,
But then who's countin'?
Off in the Menace Car!

MENACE 1

NIGEL PARKINSON

Mum is next, we got her perfume,
Soon the pong is filling the room.
Choking, crying, feels like she's dying.
Look at the old girl zoom.
Got the Colonel something to wear,
Made a vest from Gnasher's old hair,
Poor old buffer — see him suffer,
Lots of fleas still in there!
TO THE COLONEL
Sergeant Slipper gets a new hat,
It lights up, well just fancy that!
We're so cunning, see him coming,
Doesn't he look a prat?
TO SGT. SLIPPER
NONE LEFT FOR YOU, READERS — YOU'LL BE PLEASED TO HEAR! A VERY MENACING CHRISTMAS FROM ALL OF US!

O, car of wonder, what a sight,
Rev her up and hold on tight.
Off we're speeding, still proceeding,
Ride with us, you'll be all right!
MENACE 1
MENACE 1
STINK BOMBS.
SUPA SOAKER
Yon's a babe on Beanotown Plain,
Toys we bring to drive folk insane,
Poor old Trevor, well I never,
Won't be the same again.
Not much sense to offer have I.
For poor Rasher, got a pork pie,
He's not happy, this pink chappie,
Wallops me in the eye.
BOK!

DENNIS and the DINMAKERS
MUSICAL MAYHEM
NEW WAVE
BLAST!
WHOOSH!
PLEASANT THOUGHTS!
DENNIS and the DINMAKERS
MUSICAL MAYHEM
ROCK
POUND!
THUD!
SCREECH!
TWANG!
GNASH!
BEANO ROCK
CHOMP!
CRUNCH!
DENNIS and the DINMAKERS
MUSICAL MAYHEM
The BLUES
SWOOSH!
SWOOSH!
BLUEBERRY JUICE
SKIP!
SKIP!
SKIP!
DENNIS and the DINMAKERS
MUSICAL MAYHEM
R'N'B
RUPERT N BASIL
PERFUME EMPORIUM
SHOCKWAVE!
BLAST!
CLUNK!
CLONK!
THUD!
PERFUME PONG
SCENTED NIFF
RNB
SMASH!
CRASH!
SHATTER!

CAN'T GET YOU OUT OF MY SHED!
DENNIS and the DINMAKERS
BANGA!
BOOM!
BANGA!
BOOM!
BOOM!
WE LUV
OW!
INFERNAL DIN!
SIMPLY EAR-SHREDDING!
MY POOR SOFT EARS!
ROSE PETALS

IF WE WERE POP STARS...
GNOASIS
TOP OF THE POPS
WOW! HANDSOME EYEBROWS!
IF I WAS A POP STAR...
MY TRAFFIC CONES!
MINDONNA
IF I WAS A POP STAR...
OW! ME FINGERS!
SLAM!
'ERBERT JOHN
IF WE WERE POP STARS...
GIMME BACK MY MOP TOPS!
THE BASHLES

BUMPER EDITION WITH FREE PUZZLE BOOK
Dec 24th - 31st. 2005 No. 3310. www.beanotown.com
£1.58
THE BEANO
IT'S CHRISTMASTIME, THERE'S NO NEED TO BE AFRAID.
YES, THERE IS, COS I'VE GOT THIS BRAND NEW SPADE ...
SING ALONG INSIDE –
SLOOSH!
FREE 64 PAGE PUZZLE BOOK!

Dennis the Menace
...AND IN MY WORLD THERE'S PLENTY WAYS TO GIVE ME SMILES OF JOY. FIRE A SNOWBALL AT SOME GIRLS AT CHRISTMASTIME!
WHEEEEEE!
PYOING!
WHUMP!
BUT SAY A PRAYER, PRAY FOR THE SOPPY ONES. AT CHRISTMASTIME THEY'RE SOFT, AND THAT CAN'T BE MUCH FUN. LOTS OF SNOW OUTSIDE THEIR WINDOW, THAT'S WHY THEY SHAKE WITH DREAD AND FEAR. COS I HAVE MADE A MENACE SNOWMAN, AND IT'S REDUCED THEM ALL TO TEARS...
SHIVER! WHIMPER! TREMBLE!
TINKLE! CHING!!
CHOMP! GNASH!
CHINKLE! TING!
DOGGY TOY
THAT'S NOT CHRISTMAS BELLS THAT RING THERE, IT'S THE GNASHING JAWS OF DOOM. WELL TONIGHT HE'S GOT A CHRISTMAS BONE TO CHEW.

AND THERE WON'T BE SNOW AT GRANNY'S HOUSE THIS CHRISTMASTIME.
SHE GOT A STOCK OF PEPPERMINTS FOR LIFE.
NOW JUNGLE THERE CAN GROW,
SHE GIVES OFF SUCH A GLOW –DOESN'T FEEL LIKE CHRISTMASTIME AT ALL
GLOW!
MELT!
MELT!
SKIP
GRANNY'S PEPPERMINT SUPPLY (EXTRA HOT!)
HERE'S TO YOU, CHRISTMAS
GNISSES EVERYONE.
HERE'S TO DEN, THOUGH
HE'S NOT THE PERFECT SON.
ALL THE BEST AT CHRISTMASTIME TO ALL!
CHINK!
CHINK!
FEED THIS GIRL!
FEED ME LOADS AT CHRISTMASTIME!
FEED THIS GIRL!
FEED ME LOADS AT CHRISTMASTIME AGAIN.
WHIZZ!
LIQUIDIZE!
WHIRR!
WHACK!

HAIR WE GO!
GNEESH!
GOOD DOG, GNASHER! GIMME ALL THAT HAIR! IT'S JUST WHAT WE NEED FOR SOME HAIRY MENACING. WATCH THIS!
FIRST, EAT A STICKY JAM SANDWICH.
ADD GNASHER'S HAIR AND – INSTANT BEARD AND MOUSTACHE!
THROW!
SEE? I LOOK JUST LIKE THAT BLOKE THAT'S PLAYING HIS PIANO IN CONCERT TODAY!
CONCERT
RIMSKI CORSETOFF
-TODAY-
GNOT HALF!
'SPECIALLY AFTER I GEL MY HAIR.
CONCERT
GNOW YOU'RE HIS TWIN!
HAIR GEL
GUESS WHO'S GOING TO THE SOPPY CONCERT – THE SOFTIES, OF COURSE!
HOW WODERFUL TO BE GOING TO A LOVELY PIANO RECITAL!
BEST OF ALL, THAT NASTY DENNIS RUFFIAN WOULD NEVER GO!
NOR HIS FRIGHTFUL HOUND! THEY JUST DON'T LIKE GOOD MUSIC!
HEE-HEE! THEY'RE IN FOR A BIG SURPRISE!
GNOT A PLEASANT ONE!
THE RIMSKI CORSETOFF TINKLING IVORY TOUR
Shortly –
EIN BEAUTIFUL MELODY! LA! LA! LA!
RIMSKI CORSETOFF
AHA! HERE COMES THE REAL RIMSKY.
VIT EIN LOVELY CHORUSKI! LA! LA! LA!
CLIP!
I KNEW GNASHER'S OLD LEAD WOULD COME IN HANDY.
And –
I SAYSKI! VOT IS GOING ON?
TIE THE OTHER END HERE...

GNEE-HEE!
OUT FOR A SPIN, RIMSKY? THAT'S NICE!
AARGHSKI!
EEKSKI!
WAASKI!
YIKESSKI!
HEE-HEE!
OOHSKI! I DON'T FEEL WELL! I'M GOING HOMESKI. THE CONCERT IS OFFSKI!
JUST AS PLANNED, I'LL TAKE RIMSKI'S PLACE AT THE CONCERT!
SPARE JACKETS
So, at the Concert Hall –
LADIES, GENTLEMEN AND SOFTIES, PLEASE WELCOME ...RIMSKI CORSETOFF!
RIMSKI CORSETOFF
HOORAH!
SPIFFING!
Wait for it, readers!
FUNNY! NOTHING'S HAPPENING. MAYBE THERE'S SOMETHING JAMMED UNDER THE LID!
NOT A SOUND!
THERE IS –GNASHER!
PYOING!
LIFT!
RIMSKI CORSETOFF
OOOOOO! THAT NAUGHTY DOGGY! AND HIS LOUD GUITAR!
WHAT A DIN!
OUR DELICATE EAR DRUMS!
HEY! THAT SOUNDS COOL! LET'S CHECK IT OUT!
TWOINNG!
EXIT
TWANG!
GREAT TUNES!
SOUNDS AWFUL! LET US OUT OF HERE!
So –
YOWL!
TWANGGG!
TWANG!
GBOOGIE!
CRASH!
HA-HA! WE KNOW WHAT THE LISTENERS REALLY WANT! THRASH IT, GNASHER!
DDINK!

PLUG UNPLUGGED

ARE YOU LOATHSOME TONIGHT?
ARE YOUR FEATURES A FRIGHT?
ARE YOU SAD YOU'RE NOT GORGEOUS LIKE ME?
DO YOUR FRIENDS RUN AWAY,
CAN THEY NOT LOOK YOUR WAY?
I'M AFRAID I CAN NOT DISAGREE!
ARE YOU SAD THAT THE GIRLS ARE
NOW SCREAMING MY NAME?
I'M SO BLOOMIN' ATTRACTIVE,
SURELY I'M NOT TO BLAME.
WELL I JUST MUST EXPLAIN,
YOU'RE SO FRIGHTFULLY PLAIN.
TELL ME, DAN, ARE YOU LOATHSOME TONIGHT?

TWANG!
PLINK!
PLONK!
TAP!
TAP!

ARE YOU LOATHSOME TONIGHT?
IS YOUR FACE NOT QUITE RIGHT?
DO YOU LONG FOR MY TOP BEAUTY TIPS?
STICK YOUR THUMB UP YOUR NOSE,
PULL AS FAR AS IT GOES.
GO CROSS-EYED AS YOU PUCKER YOUR LIPS.
YOU'LL STILL BE QUITE UGLY, BUT GIVE IT A TRY.
AT LEAST YOU WON'T BE SUCH A HIDEOUS GUY.
LOOKS LIKE YOU'RE IN GREAT PAIN -
I MUST ASK YOU AGAIN,
TELL ME, SID, ARE YOU LOATHSOME TONIGHT?

TUG!

PLINK! PLONK!

TWANG!

YOUR GUITAR'S MADE IN SPAIN - SEEMS IT'S GONE TO YOUR BRAIN!
NOW YOU'RE EVEN MORE GRUESOME TONIGHT!

MY FAVOURITE THINGS
BY GNASHER
Draintops on noses and scaring soft kittens. Sharp stinging nettles and posties well bitten.
BUTCH
Big fat pork sausages in a long string – These are a few of my favourite things!
Cream covered bonies and dog food pot noodles. Hair gel and mince smells and gnashing Walt's poodle.
Wild geese that fight with swing of their wings – These a few of my favourite thi

Boys in white shell suits
with blue satin sashes,
Jumping in puddles and
making big splashes.
Gnashing in Winter and
gnashing in Spring –
These are a few of my
favourite things!
&
&
&
When it's bath night,
When those weeds sing,
When life seems a drag-
I simply remember my favourite things
And then my tail starts to wag!
DS

Aiken Drum
AN OLD SCOTTISH NONSENSE SONG drawn by HUNT EMERSON
There was a man lived in the moon,
Lived in the moon, lived in the moon,
There was a man lived in the moon -
And his name was Aiken Drum!
And he played upon a ladle,
A ladle, a ladle,
He played upon a ladle,
And his name was Aiken Drum!
SKWAWK
SKWONK
AIKEN DRUM - 1

And his hat was made of
good cream cheese,
Good cre ese,
Good c ese,
His k de of
good ese -
And his name was
Aiken Drum!
And his coat was made of
good roast beef,
And his name was
Aiken Drum!
And he played upon a ladle,
A ladle, a ladle,
He played upon a ladle -
And his name was
Aiken Drum!
And his buttons were made of
penny loaves,
WEEVILS
And his name was
Aiken Drum!
And his breeks were made of
haggis bags,
HOOTS!
HOOTS!
HOOTS!
HOOTS
And his name was
Aiken Drum!
AIKEN DRUM - 2

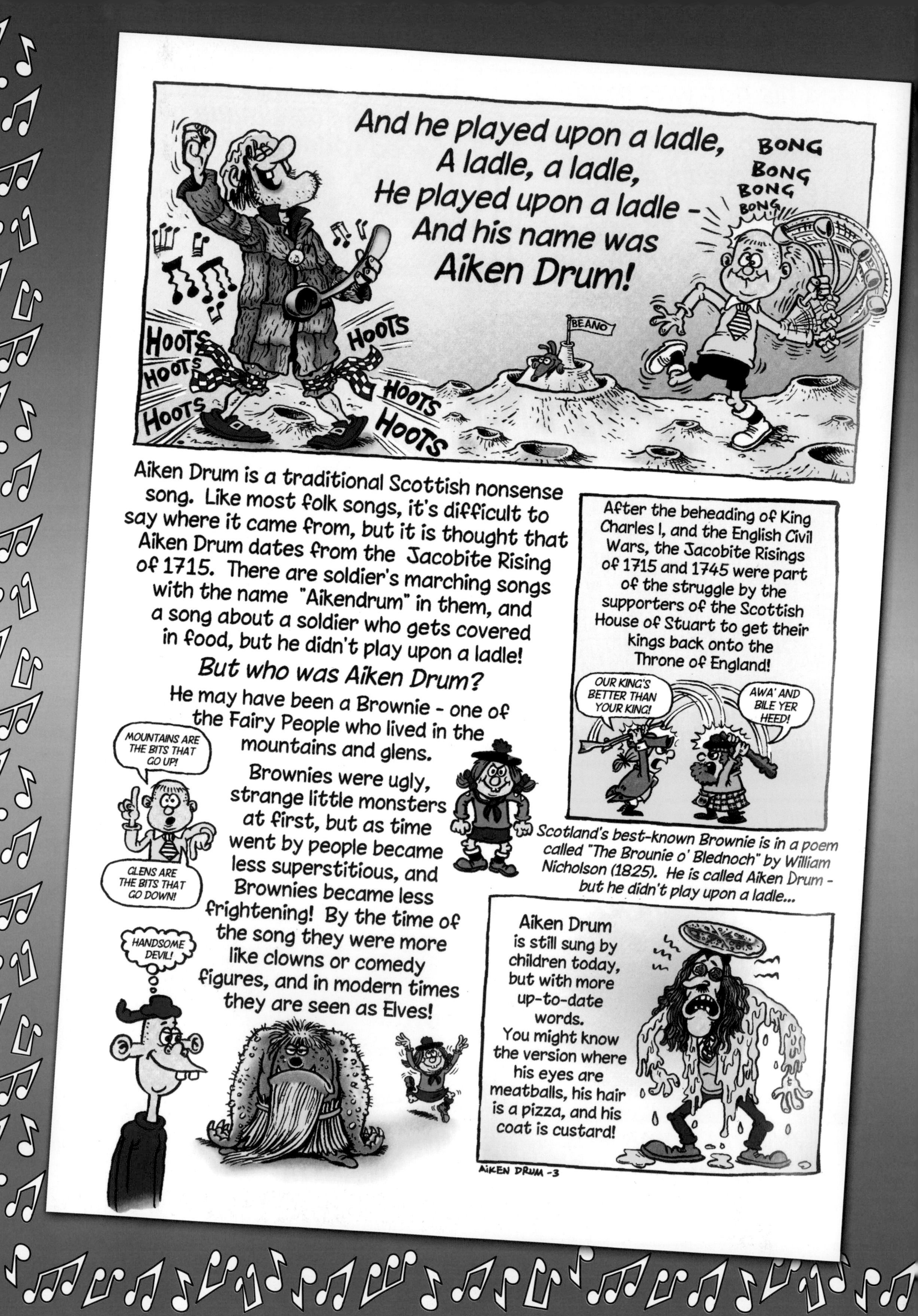
And he played upon a ladle,
A ladle, a ladle,
He played upon a ladle -
And his name was
Aiken Drum!
BONG
BONG
BONG
BONG
HOOTS
HOOTS
HOOTS
HOOTS
HOOTS
HOOTS
BEANO
Aiken Drum is a traditional Scottish nonsense song. Like most folk songs, it's difficult to say where it came from, but it is thought that Aiken Drum dates from the Jacobite Rising of 1715. There are soldier's marching songs with the name "Aikendrum" in them, and a song about a soldier who gets covered in food, but he didn't play upon a ladle!
After the beheading of King Charles I, and the English Civil Wars, the Jacobite Risings of 1715 and 1745 were part of the struggle by the supporters of the Scottish House of Stuart to get their kings back onto the Throne of England!
OUR KING'S BETTER THAN YOUR KING!
AWA' AND BILE YER HEED!
But who was Aiken Drum?
He may have been a Brownie - one of the Fairy People who lived in the mountains and glens.
MOUNTAINS ARE THE BITS THAT GO UP!
GLENS ARE THE BITS THAT GO DOWN!
Brownies were ugly, strange little monsters at first, but as time went by people became less superstitious, and Brownies became less frightening! By the time of the song they were more like clowns or comedy figures, and in modern times they are seen as Elves!
Scotland's best-known Brownie is in a poem called "The Brounie o' Blednoch" by William Nicholson (1825). He is called Aiken Drum - but he didn't play upon a ladle...
HANDSOME DEVIL!
Aiken Drum is still sung by children today, but with more up-to-date words.
You might know the version where his eyes are meatballs, his hair is a pizza, and his coat is custard!
AiKEN DRUM -3

SPECIAL 16-PAGE STORY
THE BEANO VARIETY SHOW

STRIKE UP THE BAND!
TAP! TAP! TAP!
PARAPAPUM! PARAPAPUM!
PARP! PARP!
PLUCK! PLUCK!
PLINK! PLINK!
Back stage —
OK — I'M READY! RAISE THE CURTAIN!
THAT'S MY JOB!
HOIST ROPE
CURTAIN ROPE
And —
WAH!
ZOOOM!
SNIGGER!
On stage —
WELCOME TO THE BEANO VARIETY SHOW — AND THE FIRST ACT IS . . .
13

SPLAT!
OOFYAH!
NO MENTION OF A HIGH DIVE ACT HERE.
WHAT A PLUMMET!
I'LL TAKE OVER. THE FIRST ACT IS THE AMAZING SABRE THE BRICK WITH HIS LOVELY ASSISTANT FRANKIE.
HEEL, SABRE! HEEL!
STAY, BOY!

HE DID IT! HOW ABOUT THAT. ISN'T SABRE WONDERFUL?
WONDERFULLY BORING, I'D SAY.
GO TO YOUR MASTER, SABRE!
WALLOP!
S-SABRE LOVES ME! HE K-KISSED ME! BURRLE!
TWITTER!
TWITTER!
BETTER GET THE BAND TO PLAY INSTEAD.

SOON PUT A STOP TO THAT!
TWANG!
PTCHOO!
PTCHOO!
PTCHOO!
PTCHOO!
SNAP

IF YOU WANT MUSIC — ER — MUSIC YOU SHALL HAVE! HERE ARE DENNIS AND THE DINMAKERS!
BEAM!
BEAM!
WRIGGLE!
SQUIRM!
DEAFENING SILENCE!!
WON'T TAKE A MOMENT TO MAKE SURE OUR INSTRUMENTS ARE OUT OF TUNE.
LIGHTS
ON
OFF
TEE-HEE!
CRASH!
BOOM!
TWANG!
THUD!
WH-WHO PUT THE LIGHTS OUT?
AHEM! THAT CERTAINLY WAS A DIN, EH, FOLKS?
AND NOW, THE FABULOUS, THE SENSATIONAL "FLYING FAT BOYS"!

FATTY FUDGE WILL NOW DO AN AMAZING NINE SOMMERSAULTS!
THAT'S WHAT HE THINKS!
RAZZ-RAZZ!
SNAP!
ULP! OH, DEAR! MAKE THAT NO SOMMERSAULTS.
THAT WAS ALL YOUR FAULT, FAT OAF!
WHO ARE YOU CALLING FAT, LARD BUCKET?

BIFF!
THUMP!
SMACK!
ERK! GET THEM OFF STAGE — QUICK!
NO SOONER SAID THAN DONE!
CRANK
LEVER FOR TRAP DOOR
WHOOOOSH!
BZZZZT!
WELL, THAT'S THE END OF THAT ACT. NOW, WHO'S NEXT?
OF C-COURSE — IT'S THE BEANO DANCE TROUPE. HOW COULD I FORGET?
KICK!
HOWDY, FOLKS!
The Beano Dance Troupe.

THERE'S NOT A LOT OF LAUGHS IN THIS.
DANCERS NEED SLIPPERY FLOORS.
YERK!
BETTER . . .
WOOPS!
WHUMP!

THE NEXT ACT IS ME . . .
. . . THE DARING YOUNG Y-YOUNG PLUG ON THE H-HIGH-WIRE . . .
TOO GOOD A CHANCE TO MISS!
. . . ER — MAKE THAT LOW-WIRE!
PULL!
TWANG!
NO — HIGH-WIRE IS MORE FUN!

I'M NOT WORRIED. I HAVE A SAFETY-NET.
PUSH
SNIGGER — MISSED!
SPLAT!

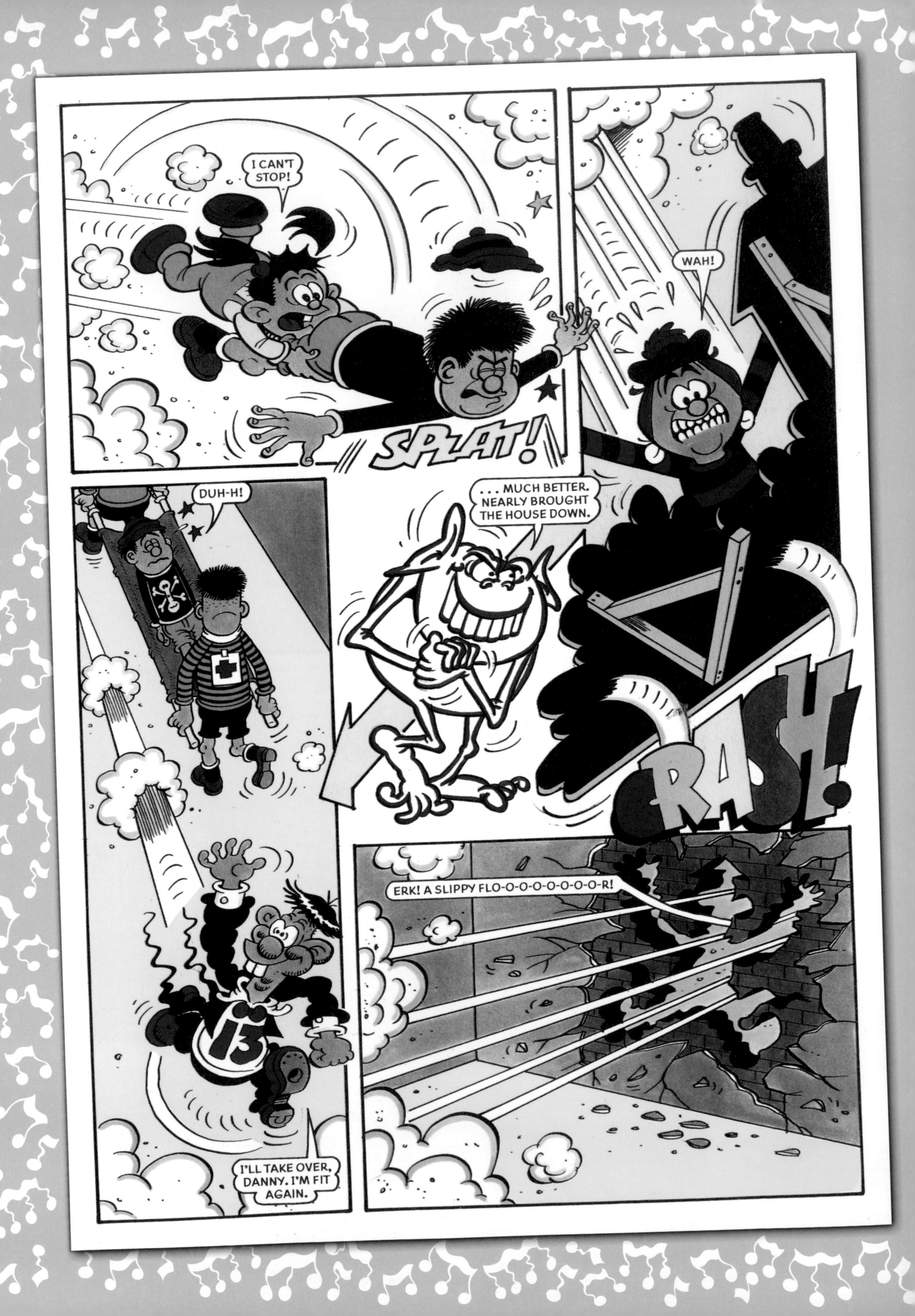
I CAN'T STOP!
SPLAT!
WAH!
DUH-H!
. . . MUCH BETTER. NEARLY BROUGHT THE HOUSE DOWN.
CRASH!
I'LL TAKE OVER, DANNY. I'M FIT AGAIN.
ERK! A SLIPPY FLO-O-O-O-O-O-O-O-R!

I'LL JUST REMOVE PLUG WHILE YOU WELCOME THE NEXT ACT — THE GREAT DODGERO!
I WILL PRODUCE A RABBIT FROM THE HAT!
THAT'S WHAT YOU THINK, CHUM!
PULL
LET'S SEE YOU DODGE YOUR WAY OUT OF THIS, CACKLE!
Then —
BOO! CHEAT!

ER — FOR MY NEXT TRICK I NEED A GENT'S WATCH.
PLOP!
BE VERY CAREFUL WITH THAT — OR ELSE!
NO PROBLEMS!
A QUICK SWITCH!
SWIPE!
RUBBER
THAT WATCH HAD BETTER BE OK.
IT WILL — DON'T WORRY!
CRUNCH!
ULP! NOW YOU CAN WORRY!
SNARL!

AT LEAST THE GREAT DODGERO MADE HIMSELF AND HIS DAD DISAPPEAR.
ZOOM!
WHAT'S GOING TO GO WRONG NEXT? CAN'T UNDERSTAND ALL THESE DISASTERS.
I CAN, YOU THICK LOT!
READ THESE AND YOU'LL SEE WHY THINGS WENT WRONG.
THE BEANO
THAT'S WHY!
G-GULP! NOW THEY'RE BEANO READERS THEY CAN SEE ME.

ZAP! BIFF! KAPOW! CRACK! SPLAT!
Painfully soon —
G-GROAN! I WISH N-NOBODY COULD S-SEE ME N-NOW!
BUT IT'S LUCKY THEY CAN, BECAUSE . . .
JUGGLE!
PARP!
POP!
TAP-TAP...
TAP-TAP...
YOU'RE GOING TO PERFORM ALL THE ACTS!
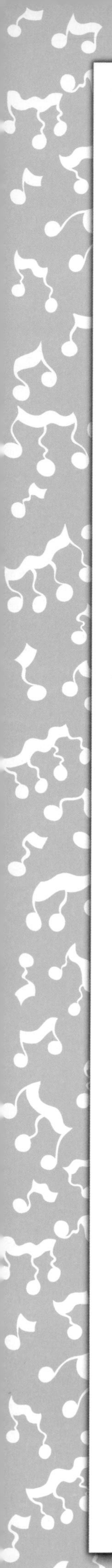

SHOCKING
ALL OVER THE WORLD!
Curly.
TWANG
PLINK
Pie-face.
BOOM -DA- BOOM
WE'RE THE DINMAKERS! YEAH! YEAH! YEAH!

YOU'RE THE DINMAKERS! NO-NO-NO!
ZIP!
Z-Z-Z-ZIP!
COVER
COVER
COVER
COVER
AW!
PEOPLE HAVE BEEN COMPLAINING ABOUT THE NOISE YOU MAKE!
WHO, DAD?
COVER
SNIGGER!
EH?
NO CHANCE, MY LAD!
CLAMP
CLAMP
CLAMP
CLICK!
CLAMP
OH, NO!
THERE'S TO BE NO MORE PLAYING AROUND HERE EVER AGAIN, DENNIS!
WHAT?!?
WAG!
Sergeant Slipper.
Look at their snaps!
WE'RE GOING ON OUR "SHOCKING ALL OVER THE WORLD" TOUR!
HOORAY!
PEACE AT LAST!

HIM FOR A START!
GULP!
BEANOTOWN CEMETRY
QUIET!
RIP
EEP THE
SE DOWN!
WE WERE PRACTISING FOR A CONCERT TONIGHT!
WAVE
COME ON, DINMAKERS — GIVE ME A SMILE!
WHY, DENNIS?
BECAUSE I'M TAKING PASSPORT PHOTOGRAPHS OF YOU!
COOL!
SNAP
CLICK
CLICK
SNAP
CLICK
GNCOOL!
YOU CAN HAVE YOUR INSTRUMENTS BACK IN THAT CASE!
CLICK
CUDDLE
So—
HEY, WORLD, NOW YOU GOT THE CHANCE . . .
'BYE MENACES
TO FRANCE
LE PUFF PUFF

. . . WE'RE OFF AND ROCKIN', SO LOOK OUT, FRANCE!
AARGH! LES DINMAKERS!
BONJOUR!
QUICK! GET WORKING!
EXTRA SECTION 1
EXTRA SECTION 2
EXTRA SECTION 3
EXTRA SECTION 4
GERMANY
BORDER
FRANCE
HURRY! HURRY!
NEARLY THERE!
Until —
EXTRA SECTION 1578
GASP!
PHEW! MADE IT!
EH?
WELCOME TO GERMANY
LE PUFF PUB
GERMANY? WHAT HAPPENED TO FRANCE?

RUM-TUM-TIDDLE-TUM
TUM-TIDDLE-TUM,
TUM-TIDDLE-TIDDLE-TUM-
TAP! TAP!
SLAP!
SLAP!
CLAP! CLAP!
HEY! THAT LOOKS FUN! LET'S TRY IT!
TWANG-TWANG-TWANGLE-TWANG!
TWANG-TWANGLE-TWANG!
TWANGLE-TWANG-TWANGLE!
BOOM
YEOWL! MY POOR KNEES!
GNEE-HEE!
SLAP!
SLAP
SLAP
SLAP
SLAP
SLAP
WHEEE

HOW DARE YOU SLAP POOR BORIS' KNEES SO MUCH!
THROB! THROB!
ERK! LET'S GO, DINMAKERS!
DER SAUSAGE FACTORY
QUICK! INTO THIS BASKET!
DER SAUSAGE BASKET
SAUSAGE FILLING ON ↔ OFF
TURN
THIS SAUSAGE SKIN GIVES ME AN IDEA!
TUG!
HORRIBLE SPICY SAUSAGE BREATH
IF WE TIE THE ROPES TO THE SAUSAGE SKINS . . .
DER SAUSAGE BASKET
TIE
. . . LIKE THIS, WE HAVE OUR VERY OWN . . .
INFLATE
DER SAUSAGE BASKET
. . . HOT AIR BALLOON! YAHOO! WE'RE OFF ON O
WORLD TOUR AGAIN!
RISE

BAH! LOST THEM!
BUMP!
HEH!
Inside the factory —
OH, NO! GNASHER'S GOT THE SCENT OF SPICY SAUSAGES!
BLOOP
BLOOP
SNIFF! SNIFF!
SPICY SAUSAGE NIFF!
CHOMP! DELICIOUS!
LEAP
. . . AND USE GNASHER'S HOT, SPICY BREATH . . .
VILE HOT SPICY BREATH
DER SAUSA BASK
Soon —
LET'S PLAY A CONCERT IN THE AIR ABOVE SWITZERLAND!
HEY, YOU SWISS, WON'T YOU LISTEN TO THIS! GONNA PLAY THE KIND A MUSIC THAT YOU JUST CAN'T MISS!
SWISS BORDER
CHEESE
CHEESE
RUMBLE
RUMBLE

Suddenly —
PLINK!
PLONK!
TWANG!
SWOOSH!
RUMBLE!
I'M STUCK!
SWISS CHEESE
WE'VE GOT TO GET RID OF THEM!
OOH!
MOO!
So —
THIS SHOULD DO IT!
ERK! WE'RE HEADING BACK THE WAY WE CAME!
BLAST OF AIR!
BLOW!
BLOW
BLOW
PARP
PARP
PARP
BLAST!
BLAST OF AIR!

But—
OOPS! WE'RE FLYING PAST BRITAIN!
ZOOM
IRELAND
BRITAIN
On board a nearby plane —
SOUNDS LIKE THUNDER!
BOOM! BOOM!
BOOM-DA-BOOM!
NO! IT'S GNASHER PLAYING HIS DRUMS!
Eventually —
COO! AMERICA!

YIKES! WE'VE BEEN BURST BY THE STATUE OF LIBERTY!
DRIFT
BANG!
BURST
FISSSSSSSSS
WAAAH!
LOOK! A HUGE CROWD! THEY MUST HAVE KNOWN WE WERE COMING!
BASEBALL STADIUM
WE'RE THE DINMAKERS! YEAH! YEAH! YEAH!
TWANG
BOOM
PLONK
HEY! QUIT THE NOISE! WE GOT A BASEBALL MATCH TO PLAY HERE!
BASEBALL STADIUM
COACH
BOOM-DA BOOM

SORRY, BUT I CAN'T HEAR YOU FOR ALL THE NOISE WE'RE MAKING!
SWISH
SPIN
SWISH
RIGHT, PITCHERS, LET 'EM HAVE IT!
COACH
THROW
THROW
THROW
RIGHT, DINMAKERS, LET THEM HAVE IT!
SWISH
SWISH
SWISH
WHEE!
WHEE!
WHEE!
WHEE!
THWACK!
WAAH!
THWACK!
EEK!
THWACK!
AARGH!
THWACK!

GREATEST HOME RUNS WE'VE EVER SEEN!
AMAZING!
CLAP! CLAP!
BOW!
BOW! BOW!
BOW!
BOW!
NEVER MIND A HOM RUN — WHAT ABOU RUN HOME?
On board —
WE'LL ENTERTAIN THE PASSENGERS!
WE'RE PLAYIN' IT LOUD OUT HERE ON THE OCEAN, GOTTA GET THIS SHIP A REAL ROCKIN' MOTION!
TINKLE
CRASH
SHATTER SHATTER
WE'LL PLAY HERE INSTEAD!
PLINK
STOMP
OI! STOP THAT DIN!
EH?
WHO SAID THAT?

HMMM!
COACH
AFTER THAT DISPLAY, YOU'LL GO HOME IN STYLE, GUYS!
COACH
And—
Queen Elizabeth 2
COACH
ROLLIN'
CAN'T TAKE ANY MORE OF THIS! GROOGH!
UHH! I'M SEASICK!
RUFF!
PUFF! PANT!
YOU'VE BEEN BANNED FROM THIS SHIP, WE'RE PUTTING YOU ON A DESERT ISLAND!
LOWER
SPLUTCH
THROW
CAN'T A WHALE HAVE A SNOOZE IN PEACE?
EEK!
GNWAAH!
HELP!

W-O-W-!
BLOW
BLOW
I'VE HAD ENOUGH OF YOU LOT!
OOYAH!
WHUMP!
TO BRITAIN
WAAAAAH!
WHEEE
LOOK! IT'S THE DINMAKERS AGAIN!
HA! HA! KEEP GOING, YOU LOT!
Queen Elizabeth 2
Back in Beanotown —
OH, NO! THEY'RE BACK!
LOOKS LIKE OUR PEACE IS OVER!
WHEE
SMASH!
CRASH!
BUMP!
S/P/L/A/T
T/H/U/D

But —
WE WON'T BE ABLE TO PLAY!
SOB! WE LANDED ON OUR GEAR!
GROAN! THEY'RE ALL SMASHED UP!
YES!
YAHOO!
OH-HO!
HUMPH!
GNUMPH!
But —
OH, NO! WE CAN'T HAVE THIS, MEN!
AGREED!
WE'LL GET YOU NEW INSTRUMENTS, DINMAKERS!
EH? WHY ARE THESE BUSINESSMEN DOING THAT?
A. TWANG
MUSICAL INSTRUMENTS
GUITARS
DRUM KITS
PUSH

And, so —
TWANG
PLINK!
PLONK!
BOOM-DA-BOOM!
CRASH
TINKLE
CRASH
BAH! MY WINDOWS ARE BROKEN!
MY POOR EARS!
GET YOUR EARMUFFS WHILE STOCKS LAST!
GRR! MENACES!
EAR MUFFS
KEEPS ALL NOISES OUT
EAR MUFFS
A. PAYNE Glazier
I'M GOING TO PELT THEM WITH FRUIT!
RUB! RUB!
LOTS OF WORK FOR ME REPAIRING WINDOWS!
HA! HA!
B. TURNIP FRESH FRUIT
TOSS!
FRESH FRUIT! BUY YOUR FRESH FRUIT TO THROW AT THE DINMAKERS HERE!
HA-HA! THE DINMAKERS KEEP THESE MEN IN BUSINESS.
ACHE!
THROB!